Reflections on 75+ Years of Teagle Machinery

By Fred Teagle
and Tony Mansell

Foreword

Charting the history of Teagle Machinery Limited from small beginnings to a world-renowned machinery manufacturer was a story that needed telling – 75 years of design, development and manufacture on the Blackwater site. It also seemed the right time to put on record the wonderful stories and memories of the early days from some of our employees and former employees – but, how to turn it into a book?

It was Christmas 2012 when I first asked Tony Mansell if he would be interested in helping me write a book marking the 75th anniversary of Teagle Machinery

Blackwater Factory Site September 2014

Ltd. We were enjoying a glass of wine at Geoff and Jenny Osborne's house at the time. I cannot be sure how much he had imbibed but I understood his response to be in the affirmative. Admittedly, about six months had passed before I again made contact but I did detect that he was a little hazy about the commitment that he had made. Perhaps, now, as I look back, I had slightly understated the anticipated size of the project. However, he assures me that he has enjoyed it not least because he now understands the purpose of an Edwards Pearson PR150 Bystronic CNC hydraulic press brake!

Tony has produced many books on subjects that range from brass bands to churches and from village histories to the English Civil War. He is a prolific recorder of Cornish history for which he has received the honour of being made a Cornish Bard with the name of Skrifer Istori (Writer of History).

A tremendous amount of work has gone into producing this book and a huge number of cups of coffee have been consumed as we shared our opinions on the form it would take and about which photographs should be included. Many former and existing members of staff have contributed so much to the story and I thank them all for becoming involved. In this respect, I have to give special thanks to Geoff Osborne for his considerable input and for his memory of the machines and events during the time that he has been with the company.

In addition to it being a celebration of a milestone in the life of the company it is a tribute to its founder and his wife. For Tom and Mary Teagle the company was an all-consuming passion and I hope that we have managed to convey their enthusiasm and dedication in building this world-class Cornish manufacturing business.

Whilst the purpose of this book will be clear there is also a considerable amount of social history, as you would expect from the story of a company that has been operating for over 75 years. We hope that you enjoy it.

Fred Teagle

Contents

For
Roger, Colin and their families.

Special thanks to Dinah for her patience and support.

Introduction

Teagle Machinery Ltd is situated on the long section of straight road that leads from Chiverton Cross to St Agnes, the old Truro to St Agnes Turnpike Road. Generations of youngsters have tested their cars there and have often posed the question, "How fast will she go on Teagle's straight?"

Tywarnhayle Woods, near Silverwell, was the playground of my childhood and I recall the Teagle works siren which not only signalled the end of the working day for the workers but also that it was time for us youngsters to return home as our tea would soon be on the table.

Most local folk know of Teagle's factory and are probably aware that somewhere amongst the trees there are buildings where a few bits and pieces for the farming world are made. How many, I wonder, realise that they have a world-class engineering company on their doorstep and that it was founded by a man who has been rightly described as one of Cornwall's foremost inventors and innovators?

This book is to mark and celebrate the 75th anniversary of the manufacture of farm machinery at Tywarnhayle Farm. The business stemmed from humble beginnings and grew to provide a living for many families in and beyond the boundary of St Agnes Parish. It was, and still is, a family business which punches above its weight as it competes in world markets against large multi-national manufacturing companies. It is a story which not only celebrates the history of the company but also displays the entrepreneurial skills of a board of directors who have been quick to embrace the latest ideas and technology. Teagle's products are now used across the world and discerning farmers are quick to appreciate the benefits of machinery which have not just been built to perform a task but have been designed to provide solutions.

Thanks to Fred Teagle, there is a plethora of historical information about the company and its products – a veritable archive. Add to that the recorded interviews with some past and present employees and we have a book which is brimming with technical prowess and social history.

In the company's 50th anniversary book Mary Teagle wrote the foreword. Sadly, she is no longer around to do so for this 75th anniversary book but we can borrow from her comments of 25 years ago. She talked of her involvement and her pride in the company which she and her husband had built. We know that their life centred on the business to the extent that even on their honeymoon Tom had to go to the Midlands to buy steel for the works. Indeed, business trips over the years were their only chance of seizing a few days away – holidays were for other folk. Despite this, there was no hint of regret and we are left with the certainty that she would not have had it any other way. Her pride came from the family involvement: firstly Tom, and then her three sons as they became a part of the business. She wrote too of the happy memories and finished with a poignant epitaph, "...it has been an honour to have been married to one of Cornwall's great inventors".

Our story begins some time before the first nut and bolt were fitted to the first machine. It looks at the life and times of William Thomas Teagle and then considers what he achieved and what happened as the company moved into the third generation. It gives the lie to the old Cornish expression "Towzers in one generation, towzers again in the third" which suggests that few companies survive long enough to provide for three generations. (A towzer was a poor person's apron made of hessian bags – a sure sign of poverty.)

Tony Mansell

William Thomas (Tom) Teagle

Man of Vision (1911 – 1989)

Tom Teagle
Cornish Inventor and Innovator
(Deviser ha Nowydher Kernewek)

Tom Teagle was born in 1911, near St Columb. He moved to Tywarnhayle Farm at the age of two where he lived and worked for the rest of his life.

During the late 1850s the family arrived in Cornwall when Tom's grandfather, also called Tom, brought his new wife, Lucy (née Goodman), to live at Lelant where he had taken employment as a gamekeeper on a local estate. He had previously been a messenger boy and farm worker near what is now the modern town of Milton Keynes. With information taken from the census we can see that in 1861 they were living at Rejarne Row, Lelant Downs, with their first two children. By 1871 they had moved to Castle-an-Dinas, near St Columb, where Tom had taken another job as a gamekeeper. It was there that the remainder of their 10 children were born. Lucy appeared on the census as a lace-maker, a trade which, no doubt, was due to her family's connection with the craft back home in Buckinghamshire. It was the move from Lelant to mid-Cornwall that led to the family's long-standing involvement in St Columb life.

After a few years, Tom decided to become a farmer and he took on Tregatillian, a 38-acre farm near St Columb. His son, Fred, worked the farm with him and when Fred married, it was local girl Eva Truscott whom he chose as his bride. In 1911 she gave birth to William Thomas (Tom) who was to grow into a remarkable man and is the leading character in this story.

Just two years after Tom's birth, in 1913, the family, including Tom senior, moved to Tywarnhayle Farm which they rented from the Williams family. Within a few years, Fred tried to buy the freehold but at that time the answer from the owners was an emphatic "No!"

Grandfather Tom with his grandson Tom

A young Tom Teagle – he may not have invented the wheelbarrow but he was probably already planning some improvements!

Tywarnhayle Farmhouse in 1913

As the First World War raged, Fred and Eva worked the 300-acre farm and their four children must have found the woods and river an idyllic place to grow up. Tom probably attended the Blackwater Board School but at some point he transferred to a private boarding school at Probus.

We can imagine that Tom had a natural aptitude for farm life and, at the age of 15, he left school and began helping his father run what was, in those days, a large farm. His "apprenticeship" was brief. It lasted just four years as in 1930, at the age of 19, he found himself in charge of Tywarnhayle Farm. His father had purchased Trevithick Farm at St Columb and moved there with his wife and three other children. Fred was clearly a good businessman with an apparent abundance of drive and energy and within a period of half a lifetime he provided each of his three sons with a farm.

Tom clearly revelled in the responsibility. He was a hands-on person, never happier than when he was getting "stuck in"

alongside the farm hands. It was a trait he continued to display when, in 1937, he began his second career – making agricultural machinery.

Tom had been too young to understand the implications of the outcome of the First World War but he was certainly well aware of the dangers and effects of the second conflict and, on the 25th October 1940, he had to leave his home to live in St Agnes. Truro Rural District Council had taken possession of the farmhouse "in the exercise of powers delegated by the Minister of Health under and by virtue of Regulation 51 of the Defence Regulations, 1939". In short, it had been requisitioned for occupation by war evacuees.

In 1940, children from London and other vulnerable cities were despatched to live in the more remote parts of the country. They were removed from the danger of blanket bombing which was then taking place in London and several of our other major cities and towns. Many of the children, some as young as five years old, must have been traumatised by the experience and from the comparative security of our present time we can hardly imagine how they felt as they stood on a railway platform with a name-tag pinned to their coat, a gas-mask around their neck and a small suitcase in their hand. The parting must have been emotional, tearful, and then the wait for a train to take them to an unknown destination – to live with strangers. In this case, however, two entire families came to Cornwall to live in Tywarnhayle farmhouse and it was not until the 6th February 1942 that the danger of bombing reduced and they returned home. The building was then handed back to the Teagle family.

Whether Tom fully realised what an asset his wife would be to the business we will never know but Mary Teagle's hands-on involvement and influence continued for the rest of her life. Her energy and tenacity helped make Teagle Machinery the success that it is today. Mary Teagle, née Hawke, was raised on Besoughan Farm at Colan, one of five daughters and one son. The family was heavily involved in agriculture. Her mother, Gwendoline (Gwen), was a Rundle from Colan Barton and her father, William, bred South Devon sheep which he exhibited at local agricultural shows. He was also the secretary of the West of England Ploughing Association. All of their girls married farmers' sons and there must have been a fair amount of bragging rights at family gatherings as all were involved in match ploughing.

As the farming business, and later the engineering activity, at Tywarnhayle Farm grew so did its importance to the community. Tom Teagle became one of the largest employers in the area and was

Fred and Eva with their first two children – Tom and Fred

Tywarnhayle Farmhouse – long before the drive was turned into a wide access road

known for his generosity towards many local causes. His support for his workforce, however, seems to have been in a more covert manner as described by John Veall, one of his works managers. In one painful episode John was sent to see the widow of a member of staff who had recently died. He was told to find out whether or not any financial help was required. As it transpired none was needed but the offer was made and Tom Teagle was most insistent that no one should know of it. John said that there were others instances where he did contribute but it was always done with the proviso that no one should know.

Tom once claimed that his social life was less active than any of his men, and many former employees have acknowledged that to be the case. It was apparent to them that the company was his life.

Former employee Russell Fowler had a few run-ins with Tom Teagle but, despite that, he described him as one of the best bosses you could have. He said that he was always true to his word and you knew exactly

where you stood. Others have struggled for a description of the man who was their boss for many years. To some, he seemed slightly eccentric but to Ron Hendry, another long-term member of staff, both he and Mrs Teagle were characters and there is no doubting what is meant by that in the Cornish vernacular. All agreed, however, that he was a brilliant ideas man with a steely determination, intent on doing things his way.

From the earliest days, Tom was the driving force in the design and production of a whole range of machines which have had a tremendous impact on the agriculture industry. Not all were successful but he was never afraid of failure in the pursuit of trying to resolve a problem. Ably supported by Mary, he built a company that designed and manufactured a huge range of pioneering machines. Some of them were world firsts while others were arguably ahead of their time. His legacy is a world-renowned family-owned brand name providing innovative machinery for the worldwide farming community.

The Early Years
From Farming to Engineering

In an 1847 article, Tywarnhayle Farm was described as an experimental station for testing new agricultural inventions. Considering its future under Tom Teagle that description was a huge coincidence.

On the 25th September 1869 the *Royal Cornwall Gazette* reported on "A Steam Sensation". Two Fowler steam traction engines arrived at Truro Railway Station and were driven to Tywarnhayle Farm where they were to be used for ploughing. The newspaper said, "The engines were splendid specimens of workmanship. They created an immense commotion as they proceeded down Richmond Hill and up Kenwyn Street, the noise attracting thousands of people to witness the novel sight, these engines being the first introduced into Cornwall for agricultural purposes".

In Derek Hattam's book *Cornish Land Steam in and around Perran Parish* he describes how, "They left Truro by way of the steep Chapel Hill which was easily ascended at 3 mph, onto the Redruth road, going on the journey without difficulty". Many people visited the farm to see them working and the report goes on to say, "It does its work beautifully and is said to plough not less than 10 acres per day". Tywarnhayle was referred to as a model farm occupied by Joshua Sydney Davey, a businessman and a member of the Davey family who were vested with the Manor of Mithian. Derek Hattam goes on to say that 20 horses could not have worked the land in the same time and that many local farmers decided to begin using the steam engines.

In February 1881 *The West Briton* reported that the annual Truro and District ploughing matches were held at 'Tywarn Hayle' Farm, St Agnes. It said that the weather during the morning was exceedingly rough with a very strong wind and showers of hail which were not very favourable towards making a good opening with the ploughs. There were 37 competing ploughs in the field and it opined that the land was in better condition than might have been expected.

One of the first items in the company archives is a rental lease for Tywarnhayle Farm between John Charles Williams of Caerhays Castle and Fred Teagle. Possession was from the 29th September 1913 and the period was for seven or fourteen years. At that time, the farm was two hundred and ninety four acres, two roods and seventeen poles. The annual rent was £255 – £251.3s.6d rent and £3.16s.6d tithe (an ancient system of contribution to church or state). Further fields and areas of woodland were later acquired to extend it to about 350 acres. Interestingly, the lease includes the field names but in this case they all seem to be English-descriptive rather than in Kernewek (Cornish).

Apparently the landlord's aversion to the disposal of the farm must have diminished as in 1918, and again in 1920, negotiations were under way for the sale of the freehold. Initially, the price was to be £7,000 but this was subsequently reduced to £6,750. Despite the note of optimism in the correspondence it did not happen and it is disappointing that we do not know why.

Ploughing matches continued to be a popular pastime in farming circles. We will never know when the first one took place but man is very competitive and no doubt it was not many years after he first broke the ground. Winning meant the receipt of some decent prize money but, no doubt, of equal importance were the bragging rights in the bars. The tradition was continued at Tywarnhayle Farm in 1923 and the various events and classes were advertised in this poster.

We do not know whether Tom's diversification into manufacture was a blue-flash moment but it does seem certain that it was precipitated by his own farming needs. It was certainly fuelled by his mechanical inclinations and his perception that there had to be a better way of doing things. In other words, for every invention that he created he had identified a need. He designed and built the early products and then tested them by usage on his own farm and on those belonging to other family members. Within a short time he was building a variety of labour-saving machines.

Tom Teagle was a self-taught engineer. He was a farmer who diversified into a manufacturing career with no formal engineering training, but what he lacked in knowledge he made up for with a huge slice of common sense and a steely determination to master new skills. He learned by experience and he made full use of his innovative flair and considerable talent for design. With his entrepreneurial skills, his inborn drive and commercial nous, he was soon selling his horse-drawn products to local farmers. It was an uphill battle in a very conservative industry which considered that more output automatically meant more men and more horses.

The first product
The Tipcart

Perhaps Tom Teagle had read about time and motion study, or maybe it was his in-built desire to eliminate unnecessary waste, but in the mid-1930s he decided to make a tipping cart.

It those early days the hay, straw etc was loaded by hand but he could see that some sort of tipping gear would cut the unloading time. Within a short while he was using his creation on his own farm and we can imagine the interest from his neighbours. Before long they all wanted one. It is doubtful that their reactions took him by surprise. Here was a man completely in charge of his own destiny and probably well aware that his new idea would catch on. There was now a new dimension to his business and to his life – one which he would exploit to the full. Before long, the work of the farm's blacksmith's's shop

The 1937 Tipcart
Beyond the hedge is the old blacksmith's's
shop with the granary behind

15

was no longer restricted to shoeing horses and repairing ploughs.

In 1937 Tom sold his first product and in August of that year he rendered the invoice for £48.10s.0d for the supply of three carts to E Mitchell & Sons of Penzance. Two were on CMWs (converted motor wheels) and one was on new Dunlops. This first transaction must have been hugely satisfying and we have the clear impression that he enjoyed this new aspect of his working life. Other sales followed and thus began the life of manufacturing on the Tywarnhayle site.

1937 – The Tipcart leaflet

The first tipping trailer

TEAGLE'S
Pneumatic Tyred Tipcarts

A TYPE

THE use of these vehicles will result in greater economy in horse drawn transport, whether on soft land and good or bad roads.

No noise or jarring and the design of these carts will mean more work being done with less fatigue.

This cart is designed with a large margin of safety, and only selected, well seasoned wood is used in its construction.

The large size butt is built on heavy mortised framework, reinforced with iron angles at corners, and is fitted with 9 in. detachable sideboards.

The butt is also fitted with quickly detachable tailboard and is built one inch wider at back than at front to eject any load in tipped position.

All carts are fitted with six inch pneumatic tyres on steel disc or artillery wheels.

These TIPCARTS are sold carriage paid and if they are not entirely satisfactory on fair trial they can be returned carriage paid within 14 days when the entire purchase money will be refunded.

====PRICE====

MADE BY

W. T. TEAGLE
BLACKWATER, TRURO, CORNWALL
Phone : THREEWATERS 67

1

Messrs E. Mitchell + Sons Penzance

Date		Description		£	s	d
3.8.37	1	Cart on Con. Motor Wheels		13	0	0
	1	Cart on Dunlops		22	10	0
20.8.37	1	Cart on Con Motor Wheels		13	0	0
				48	10	0
13.9.37	1	Cart on Dunlops		22	10	0
30.9.37	1	Cart on C.M.W.		13	0	0
22.10.37	1	Cart on C.M.W.	12½	15	0	0
	1	" " " with brakes	12½	16	0	0
15.1.38	1	cart on C.M.W. with brakes	12½	16	10	0
7.3.8.	1	cart on C.M.W. with Brakes		16	10	0
	1	cart chassis with brakes		12	0	0
5.4.18	1	cart on C.M.W.		15	0	0
12.4.18	1	cart butt.				

Con   Page 48.

25/9/37 by cheque £48 10 0

11.12.37 By cheque 27 0 0

Two carts returned.

Paid by cheque £56 8 9

The first transaction

One of Tom's first creations – a converted Leyland lorry made a handy tractor. It required two gearboxes to achieve a slow-enough speed and is shown here towing a home-made cabbage planter.

Potato Planters
Seed Drills – Transplanters

In September 1939 Britain was at war and with that news went the call for this island nation to be able to feed itself. Farm production would have to increase to meet the demand.

1941 – The Mk 1 Potato Planter leaflet

THE W. T. TEAGLE POTATO PLANTING MACHINE
(PATENTS PENDING)

This machine plants potatoes as accurately as hand planting at a rate of four to six acres per day with a saving of 75% of the cost. The machine does five operations at one time, i.e. opens the drills, plants the potatoes, covers the potatoes lightly with soil, sows the fertilizer and lastly splits back the drills. This method of placing the fertilizer above the potatoes in the drill has several advantages. Two-row design permits of central draught to tractor without tractor wheels passing over planted rows. The drills of planter are adjustable for width, and spacing of potatoes in the rows is adjustable. The fertilizer box lifts out of chassis for cleaning by undoing one set screw. The maintenance charges of this machine are negligible barring accident.

Two of these machines have been used extensively in Cornwall during the 1941 planting season with entire satisfaction to farmers.

Write—

W.T.TEAGLE

BLACKWATER, TRURO,
CORNWALL.

It will pay you to investigate.

The illustration shows how the machine accurately plants small, large or cut potatoes without riddling.

The MK 1 Potato Planter

A new way of thinking was required, one which would reduce the reliance on manpower and exploit and embrace mechanisation. It was a tremendous challenge for inventors and innovators.

With this drive to maximise production Tom invented a novel potato planting machine. It had a series of cups on an endless chain moving through a hopper of seed potatoes. Each cup collected a potato and placed it in the ground. That was not all that it did, however. As well as planting the potato it also deposited essential fertilizer around it. It was Tom's first multi-functional piece of equipment and the first such machine in the world.

Such was the importance of this revolutionary machine that the War Agricultural Executive Committee decided to support its manufacture. Their confidence, however, was in the design rather than in Tom's capacity to produce the machine in sufficient quantities to make an impact on this country's food production. They decided that the task of manufacturing it in sufficient numbers would be undertaken by a larger, more established company. Tom was required to pass over the design, and any components already produced, to Dening & Co (1937) Ltd of Chard. In return he would receive a payment for every machine produced. The royalty agreement was signed on the 23rd March 1942 and the design, components and castings were transferred to the Somerset company.

A large number of machines were produced to the benefit of the war effort but for Tom Teagle there was a sting in the tail. Despite all the assurances, and the existence of a legal royalty agreement, he never received any payment whatsoever. Many years later, in March 1989, a letter from the Somerset Industrial Archaeological Society asked about his association with Dening of Chard. Tom's reply was caustic. Even after 47 years the bitterness was undisguised:

"My connection with Dening of Chard began and ended in 1942. My association with them could be described as financially disastrous. Converted to today's values (1989) it would mean a loss of £250,000. This was because I did not receive a penny for the production of machine parts already made and furthermore, although I had a signed licence with them for royalties, I received no remittance from them."

In his letter he reflected that it was a period when the Battle of the Atlantic was not going in our favour and there was a drive to plant as many potatoes as possible to help

The MK 1 Potato Planter

An advertisement for the Potato Planting Machine

The **W.T.TEAGLE** **Potato Planting Machine**

Patents Pending

The Last Word in Potato Planting

Unequalled for Accuracy, Speed, Durability

This machine plants potatoes as accurately as hand planting at a rate of four to six acres per day at a saving of £3 0s. 0d. per acre. The machine does five operations at one time, i.e., opens the drills, plants the potatoes, covers the potatoes lightly with soil, sows the fertilizer and lastly splits back the drills. The drills of planter are adjustable for width, and spacing of potatoes in the rows is adjustable. The fertilizer box lifts out of chassis by undoing one set screw. The maintenance charges of this machine are negligible barring accident.

Orders are now being booked for delivery in rotation.

Price **£98** free on rail

Ask your Implement Agent—or write to the Inventor

W. T. TEAGLE
Blackwater, Truro, Cornwall

W.T.TEAGLE

The original 1941 logo

avoid starvation. He readily recognised his own naivety in industrial matters and from that statement, and some other comments, it was clear that he was not impressed by the standard of management nor the integrity of the people with whom he had entered into a contract. One amusing statement related to their chief designer of machines who, he said, was adamant that if you turned a right-hand threaded bolt upside down it became a left-hand thread.

The machine received many plaudits and this April 1941 article from *Life in Cornwall* was typical. "Mr W T Teagle of Tywarnhayle Farm, Blackwater, near Truro, has invented a potato planting machine which he claims is doing the same amount of work in one day as 30 to 40 men under old-fashioned methods. One of the features of the machine – it is planting five acres of potatoes a day at present on hilly land – is that it can be worked entirely by unskilled labour. The only skilled man required is the tractor driver. This is so much the case that one of the operators working the machine is John Burton, aged 11, an evacuee from Tilbury. 'The job is easy and I've been earning five shillings a day,' he said proudly. 'I'm certainly going to be a farmer when I grow up'." The influential *Farmer & Stock-Breeder* publication also included an article in its April 1941 issue in which it praised the merits of the machine.

Many years later, former evacuee Peter Malindine, who had lived at Silverwell Post Office during the war years, recorded his wartime experience picking potatoes at Tywarnhayle Farm. It was there that he received his first pay packet – sixteen shillings for a week's work at a time when a Mars bar was 2d, if you could get them! He said, "We were issued with a metal bucket, picked spuds until it was full and then emptied it into the nearest bushel basket. A tractor was opening the ground to reveal the crop and a cart came around to collect the contents of the baskets."

In March 1942, the Ministry of Agriculture was encouraging farmers to "increase and maintain wartime food production" by guaranteeing prices for the period of the war and for a year afterwards. It also urged farmers to "add more acres to our ploughland". Apart from Tom Teagle's design efforts, his farm was also producing well as we can see from a Cornwall War Agricultural Executive Committee letter dated the 19th November 1941 which referred to the "high state of cultivation on your farm". The total cropping area offered was 137.367 acres of which about 30 acres was planted with potatoes. This was, of course, a period of general shortage when families were required to limit the amount of food that they put on the table.

1944 Potato Planter leaflet

The 1945 Transplanter – three-point linkage mounted

1944 Two-row Transplanter

In a letter to Tom, even *The Farmer & Stock-Breeder* complained that it had to omit advertisements due to a shortage of paper.

The potato planter was introduced to increase production but it was also instrumental in cutting costs and removing the back-breaking job of planting by hand. There must have been many a farm worker who gave thanks to Tom Teagle. Having said that, it is equally likely that there were many who viewed such machines as a threat to their livelihood.

A new model of the machine was introduced in 1944. It was smaller and more manoeuvrable and, with the memory of the Dening experience, Tom was careful to retain ownership of its manufacture. One attribute was its versatility – versions could also be used for cabbages, broccoli and similar produce. It became the company's first export and was equally at home with cabbages in Australia or tobacco in Rhodesia.

A seed drill is a sowing device that places seeds in the ground and then covers them with soil. Before mechanisation increased their usage, farmers could be seen laboriously plodding up and down fields casting the seeds by hand. It was a wasteful and imprecise process with considerable wastage. Jethro Tull is credited with the invention of the seed drill, in the early 1700s, although its true origins probably predate that period by hundreds of years. It is claimed that a seed drill can improve the ratio of crop yield (seeds harvested per seed planted) considerably, perhaps by as much as nine times.

Teagles produced several versions of the seed drill to meet customers' varying requirements. All had the Ferguson-designed three-point linkage which, by then, was standard on most tractors. Drills were produced in three, four, five or six row versions and supplied with or without fertilizer boxes. They were designed to be easy to clean and simple enough to be maintained by the staff on the farm, a benefit which has been embedded into design principles ever since.

Many years later, in 1997, T D Hopper Farming Ltd from Hereford wrote to say that they had acquired an old Teagle root drill and wished to restore it to working condition. They asked for information about the machine and also commented

The 1951 5-row combined Seed and Fertilizer Drill

The Jetso transplanter unit

The Jetso Transplanter

that the paintwork had deteriorated but the traces that remained suggested that the original colour was blue with red lines.

Over the years the cabbage and potato planters were improved and in 1956 came the launch of the Jetso Universal planters. These were sold in kit form and were built up with main frames of varying widths, wheels, fertilizer units, transplanter or potato planter units, a plant spacing facility or a seed drill unit. It was a pick and mix version where the customer was able to create a machine to suit his needs.

Like many of the early products, there is no defined date when production stopped. It was more a case of continuing until demand ceased.

1956 – The Pendray family testing a prototype three-row Jetso potato planter at their Caduscott Farm, Dobwalls near Liskeard.

Tom's brother-in-law John Pendray is in the driving seat and behind him is daughter Margaret. Left to right on the planter are Mary Teagle, John's son Hugh and wife, Ruth.

We have very few photographs of Tom for the simple reason that he was usually behind the camera, pressing the shutter. He wanted photographs of all his creations but was disappointed with those taken by local photographers. Apart from the quality, the photographers were never available when he needed them. To overcome this, he developed into a keen and able photographer. He always owned a good quality, medium-format camera and, of course, he was always in the right place at the right time – when the machines were new and working well. We should be grateful for his preoccupation with photography because it is the reason that we now have such a comprehensive photographic archive. In later years, Fred Teagle and Geoff Osborne, whom you will hear about later, carried on the tradition of recording on camera, which they extended to include cine and, latterly, video.

In the 1940s the roads and infrastructure that we enjoy today were but a dream, and Tywarnhayle Farm was somewhat remote with no mains electricity supply to provide power to drive the machines. From the beginning, the farmhouse and buildings were powered by home-produced electricity via a large Lister generator. As the factory grew, war surplus generators driven by reconditioned Gardner diesel engines were pressed into use. These served the company well for several years and, when it was necessary to replace them, a large Rolls-Royce diesel generator took over. This continued to be used even after the installation of a three-phase electricity supply as the combined heat and power unit provided essential heat to warm the works and to assist in the paint drying process.

There was considerable bureaucracy involved in obtaining sufficient steel and wood during the Second World War. Detailed requirements had to be listed and approved under the Control of Iron & Steel Distribution Scheme. This was, of course, understandable as the government was desperately trying to conserve supplies for the manufacture of armaments. People had to eat, however, and considerable emphasis was placed on keeping the food-chain in a healthy state. In this respect an assurance was given that in the event of damage caused by German air-raids, "necessary materials for repair will be released without formality".

The
Steerage Hoe

In time, other machines joined the range, all produced in the small workshop. One of these was the world's first tractor-mounted steerage hoe which was designed to be mounted onto a Standard Fordson tractor.

1942 – The Steerage Hoe – a world first

1945 – The Steerage Toolbar advertisement in The Farmer & Stock-Breeder of the 7th August.

It was steered through the rows of plants by the use a tiller control to the rear wheel. The steerage hoe was in such demand that manufacture was subcontracted to Boulton and Paul but Tom Teagle had learned from his dealings with Dening and he held on to the design.

In June 1942 the *West Briton and Cornwall Advertiser* included a photograph of the steerage hoe at work with the caption, "A precision steerage tool-bar, for high-speed cultivation and earthing-up of potatoes and brassica crops, at work on the farm of the inventor, Mr W T Teagle, Tywarnhayle Farm, Blackwater. Last year Mr Teagle invented a potato planter."

"It saves a lot of time – and it does a better job.."

THIS is the verdict of practical farmers who have used this new Toolbar. Here are the reasons for its greater efficiency:

It can be coupled to the tractor within ten minutes.

It practically eliminates the necessity for hand-hoeing in the case of potatoes, cabbages, broccoli and similar vegetable crops.

10,125 different combinations in the setting of the tines can be obtained in addition to using the steerage *while the machine is in operation*, thereby making it immediately adaptable for irregular rows, or for varying widths of cultivation between rows.

Independent steerage corrects side-slip or other irregularities in movement of tractor. It is manoeuvrable and easily raised above the soil for turning.

Depth of cultivation can be controlled.

Cultivating and earthing-up can be done at the same time.

The tie-bar is placed high so as to prevent bruising of normal crops.

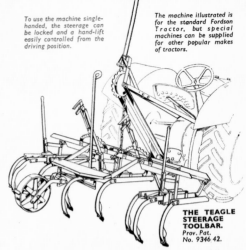

To use the machine single-handed, the steerage can be locked and a hand-lift easily controlled from the driving position.

The machine illustrated is for the standard Fordson Tractor, but special machines can be supplied for other popular makes of tractors.

THE TEAGLE STEERAGE TOOLBAR.
Prov. Pat. No. 9346 42.

Tines and other tools are always held vertical to the work.

Flexibility of the frame allows the machine to pass over uneven ground, ensuring efficient cultivation. This minimises breakages on rough land.

The only part of the machine made of cast-iron is the trailing wheel.

The Teagle Steerage Toolbar was designed by a practical farmer. Users have verified its efficiency and its advantages. It is especially suitable for all kinds of row-crop cultivation.

Diagram showing a few of the ten thousand different tine-settings which can be obtained while the machine is in motion.

The whole machine can be steered to left or right while the tines are in any position, or

The distance between each set of tines can be altered, or

Each gang of tines can be altered in width independently of the others.

The above combinations can be made without interfering with the steerage or stopping the tractor.

THE NUMBER OF THESE TOOLBARS NOW AVAILABLE IS LIMITED. MAKE EARLY APPLICATION.

The TEAGLE Steerage TOOLBAR

Manufactured by : W. T. TEAGLE (MACHINERY) LTD., Blackwater, Truro, Cornwall
Telegrams : Teagle, Truro.   Telephone : Threewaters 42

The
New Company

The Eagle-Teagle logo in use from 1943 to 1969

During the early years the business operated as W T Teagle – a sole trader. By 1943, however, its growth was such that it was considered wise to transfer operations to a limited company.

The chosen name was W T Teagle (Machinery) Ltd with Tom Teagle, his father and two brothers as the initial directors but, as the others were full-time farmers, running the manufacturing company was left to Tom. This was, of course, about six years after the engineering story began – when Tom had first sold his tipping carts. It is probable that incorporation increased the emphasis on the engineering side of the business but the farm was still Tom's main enterprise. However, he could now fully utilise his design flare and during the next few years many new products were introduced.

The art deco brooch on which the first company logo was based

Denzil Moyle began his long career with the company on the 26th March 1943. Part of his role was to keep the horses shod but the move from farming to manufacture was well underway by this time and he was increasingly involved in making parts for the machines. Denzil said, "Tom Teagle had been producing machines for some time and most of the men were involved in both the farm and the engineering side. I was in the blacksmith's shop but I also helped with carrying hay and cutting cabbages when necessary." The blacksmith's shop had been built during the early 1940s. It was where the first machines were made: the potato planters, steerage hoes and fertilizer broadcasters. Later on, as the engineering side grew, Denzil worked in the machine shop and other departments before moving to the sheet metal shop where he remained for many years. He ended his working life in the fettling shop, cleaning the work (grinding sharp edges and welds) and generally preparing the components for dipping (painting). He said, "It was a dirty and

noisy job but it paid well". After 48 years with the company Denzil retired in November 1991 but engineering was in his blood and he continued to use his skill to produce models and trophies of considerable quality. He has good memories of his time with the company and said, "They were fair and always looked after those who played fair with them, I always got on well with them".

Apart from the blacksmith's's shop, the other farm buildings also played their part. The barn became the assembly area, the Dutch barn the fabrication shop and, in February 1942, Tom's landlord agreed to the erection of a 40 feet x 26 feet machine shop next to the blacksmith's's shop. It was a timber frame and galvanised steel structure with blockwork plinth walls. According to Denzil Moyle, local men Willie Sampson and Arthur Thomas built it. Gradually the old farm buildings were replaced but in those early days they served their purpose and now, in 2015, there is only one remaining, which is used for tooling and parts storage.

Teagle produced one of the world's first tractor-mounted crop sprayers. Unfortunately the only agricultural chemicals available at the time were a Bordeaux Mixture or copper sulphate for use on potatoes and carrots and, as a consequence of this limitation, the machine appeared to have very little potential. Later, of course, crop spraying became widely used.

The
Crop Sprayer

1943 Tom Teagle watching the prototype sprayer being se

Russell Fowler was 18 when, in 1944, he called at the farm to see if there was any chance of a job. He said, "Mr Teagle was working at one of the benches when I asked him. He just turned around and looked at me for a while. Then, all he said was, 'Yes, start when you like'. That was my interview." Russell was taken on as a tractor driver but his own stories suggest that he did not cover himself in glory in that role. One of his first jobs was ploughing a large field using a three-furrow plough. He said, "The tractor wasn't 'man enough' and, apart from that, the tyres were too narrow. They tried wider tyres but it still didn't work so John Hicks, one of the other men, took over with a more powerful tractor and I had to do something else." A little later Russell was sent out with a new machine to cut hay and that did not work out too well either. He said, "I tried it in bottom gear and then in top gear but it kept jamming. Then I hit a rabbit gin and smacked the cutter right off its hinges. Mr Teagle was very good about that and told me to take it down to Denzil (Moyle) to get it welded. While that was being done I had to take the chiseller and work over the bottom of a hedge which had been removed to make two fields into one. Trouble was, they hadn't taken out the old granite gate-posts and on one of the turns I took it a bit close and smacked the wheel right off. I'd now broken two machines in an hour and I had to go in and tell Mr Teagle. All he said was, 'I'd have thought a 35-acre field was big enough'."

With the increasing emphasis on engineering it is easy to imagine that this could have been at the expense of the farm but Russell Fowler believed that this was not the case. He said, "Tom Teagle was a good farmer and always looked after his animals well". Tom later claimed that his farming methods were unconventional but profitable, alluding, no doubt, to his endless search for better working methods.

During the Second World War many prisoners of war were employed on the farm. Russell's recollections were that the Italians were not too bad, with some even remaining after the war. The Germans, however, were a different story. They were much more difficult and very reluctant to take orders. Russell said, "On one occasion I was carrying hay but I couldn't get on as they were determined to work at a pace which suited them. The boss asked me why it was taking so long and I told him that they wouldn't work any faster. He stormed out to confront them. In spite of the language difficulties, he managed to get his point across. After that it went a lot better."

Russell recalled that he was sent "up the road" a few times but each time he was given his job back. He said, "I still don't know why I was sacked but Tom didn't need much of a reason. He never seemed to have any difficulty in finding something to complain about. Mind you, I was a heller [sic] in those days. Anyway, my father told me I had to stand on my own two feet and tell him what I thought of him. I thought, me, tell Mr Teagle what I think of him! Anyway, I did get a bit braver and matters must have improved because I stayed there until I retired." We do not know why Fred Teagle's early attempt at purchasing Tywarnhayle Farm faltered but in April 1945 it was Tom Teagle who raised the question again and we can tell from one line of a letter on the file that the landlord's position was very clear. It read, "Your landlord is not desirous of selling Tywarnhayle property".

Just like any farm, the abundance of animal foodstuff attracted the rats. They were under the chicken shed, in the buildings, everywhere, and Harry Fowler was given the job of getting rid of them. Tom Teagle wanted to know what sort of poison he was going to use and whether or not it would harm the cats. "No," said Harry, "they'll be all right". The next day all the cats were dead.

"I thought you said that it wouldn't hurt the cats," said Tom.

Harry shook his head, "Well, tidn [sic] supposed to".

Whether or not he also managed to kill the rats we do not know but there were certainly no cats left to help with the task. Despite this setback in relations, Tom did entrust him with another job – blowing up the stumps of the fir trees which once lined the road from the farm towards the garage at Sevenmilestone.

By 1947, the company had established a consistent trading pattern. This was ten years after the sale of the first machine and four years after the formation of the company. We are clear on the sequence of events but it would be good to know whether this was in line with Tom Teagle's aims and ambitions back in 1937. Did he see the future as a farm supporting his passion for design or was he confident enough to predict that the engineering side would eventually eclipse the traditional farm? Perhaps the story simply unfolded and he adapted to circumstances or maybe, just like Richard Trevithick, that other Cornish inventor, it was all a part of his grand plan and he knew where his destiny lay.

Circa 1950 – Time for croust (mid-morning snack) in front of Ken Crago's drawing office.

Back row left to right: John Hicks, Gerald Blackney, Norman (Chippy) Chapman in window and John Hellings;

Mid row: Wilfred Stevens, Ivan Carpenter from Radnor, Russell Fowler turned sideways and Ronnie Wills from Wheal Rose;

Front row: Charlie Gay, Melville Strike and Ken Wills.

The building to the left is the stores – still standing in 2015

Loader-Stackers

The ancient and nostalgic scene of a great shire horse being used to operate the hay-pole

Loader-stacker prototype on MM tractor

The combination of the traditional hay-sweep and the hay-pole had served farmers well for many years. When dry, the hay was collected by the hay-sweep and brought to the pole – next to where the rick was being built.

The pole was simple in concept and in operation, using a horse to pull the long rope and a grab to raise its "handful" of hay to the top of the rick. Once deposited, the hay was piked into place by the rick builders. Of course, to lower the grab the great shire then had to walk backwards and woe betide the person leading him if they managed to get their feet in the way of this shambling giant.

The Loader-Stacker was a machine devised to combine the work of the hay-sweep and the pole. It was capable of raising half a ton of hay to a height of seven metres and its design incorporated the first push off-buck rake. The operation was completely mechanical and all controlled by one lever. It had clear advantages over the old method but for some reason there was reluctance amongst farmers to adopt this new idea. Perhaps it was the natural conservatism of the industry and this was simply a machine that was ahead of its time. Whatever the reason, few were made and it was not until tractors were fitted with external hydraulics that the fore-end loader grew in popularity.

As the company grew, those who worked the land were

generally separate from those in the manufacturing process but when the weather was too bad to work outside, the farm workers helped in the factory. One day, Russell Fowler was inside working when he was asked if he liked welding. Perhaps influenced by the wind and rain outside he replied that he did. Tom Teagle warned him that after a session with the welding torch he would hardly be able to see the next day and, in typical colourful fashion, Russell recalled that he was right. He said, "My eyes were watering and really sore but I stuck at it and that was what I did for the remainder of my time there. Anyway, a few years later he sold the land so I couldn't go back to farming."

The time when a family could exist on 20 to 30 acres was drawing to a close. Farms were amalgamating into larger units and that heralded an end to the high-volume demand of smaller items for the one-man farm. Former works manager John Veall said, "Back in the 1950s there were many such farms but as they merged we had to change to making bigger and more sophisticated machines. Another influence was the growth in agricultural contracting where larger farmers and contractors rented out their machines to the small to medium-sized farms."

EAGLE'S
REG. TRADE MARK

LOADER & STACKER

THE WAY WITH HAY

ENGINE POWER NOT MAN POWER

W. T. TEAGLE (Machinery) **LTD.,**
BLACKWATER, TRURO,
Cornwall.

Telephone No.:
THREEWATERS 42.

Telegraphic Address:
" TEAGLE, TRURO."

The first Loader-Stacker leaflet

1948 – Loader-Stacker on Fordson Major tractor

Loader-Stacker with 'push-off' option

Loader-Stacker with sheaves

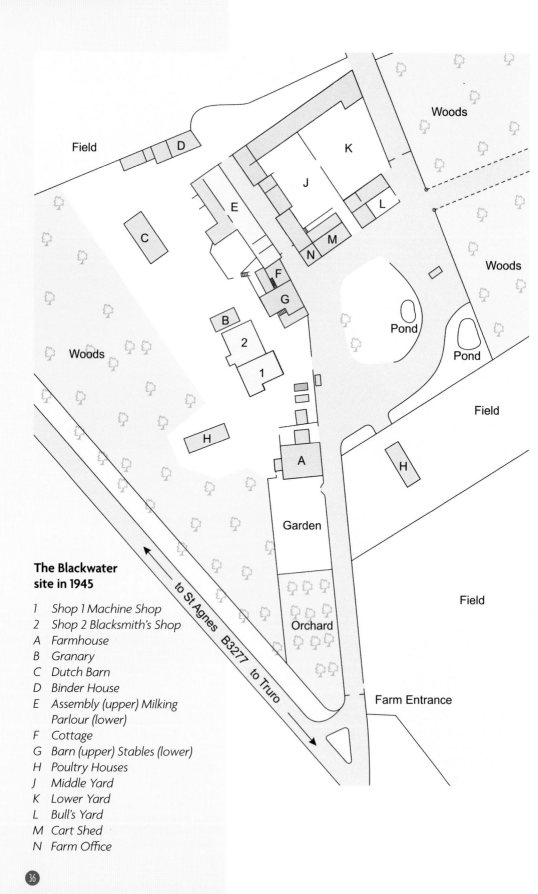

The Blackwater site in 1945

1   Shop 1 Machine Shop
2   Shop 2 Blacksmith's Shop
A   Farmhouse
B   Granary
C   Dutch Barn
D   Binder House
E   Assembly (upper) Milking
    Parlour (lower)
F   Cottage
G   Barn (upper) Stables (lower)
H   Poultry Houses
J   Middle Yard
K   Lower Yard
L   Bull's Yard
M   Cart Shed
N   Farm Office

During the early 1950s the two farmhouse front rooms were taken over and used as offices by the business – one for sales and the other, eventually, for accounts. In spite of these intrusions on the domestic scene, however, the building remained the family home and it is only in very recent years that it has been given an entirely commercial purpose. Janet Oliver from Skinners Bottom helped to run the domestic side of the house. It was her input that enabled Mary Teagle to devote so much time to the business. Janet cooked and cleaned for the family and even took care of the children and grandchildren when necessary.

By the 1950s most of the farm buildings were being used for production purposes. The old wooden Dutch barn had been enclosed and the other buildings and covered areas soon followed. Despite the change of use the old and familiar names remained and it became a trip to the duck house for nuts and bolts or to the bull's shed for sheet metal. One curious name was the Hell House, where the special steels were stored. The strange name seems to have had no agricultural connection and it probably came about because it was so dark and dingy. As demand for the machines grew so did the need for steel. In an ideal world it would have been stored inside but with insufficient covered areas some had to remain out in the open, in an area cleared in the woods – a far cry from what happens today. Former employee Mike Stephens recalled being warned not to touch the steel when it was frosty because it would stick to your skin.

Tom Teagle judging the Young Farmers' Club machinery competition at the Royal Cornwall Show at Callington in 1950. By now, Tom was well known in the world of agriculture and you can almost hear a wag saying, "I recognise Tom but who is that chap next to him?" (In case you need prompting on this, the "chap" is HRH King George VI.)

1953 — Spreading basic slag . . . where were the Health & Safety regulations in those days?

The
Broadcasters

The need to improve the accuracy of distributing artificial fertilizers led to the development of the broadcasters, a range which was to evolve over many years and become one of the company's major products.

1950 – Prototype trailed broadcaster

The Mk I Trailed Broadcaster was produced in 1950 and was the world's first production spinner broadcaster with adjustable spreading control. It was the forerunner of many thousands of fertilizer broadcasters to be manufactured at the Blackwater factory. The early models were towed behind trailers and the fertilizer was shovelled into the hopper by hand. The machine was simplicity itself, with the rotor driven by the wheels through a round belt and the hopper raised or lowered to control the flow of fertilizer.

By 1952, the reputation of the broadcaster had spread far and wide and, in July, Max Davis Proprietary Ltd of Melbourne, Australia, asked if they could manufacture and sell the machine under licence. Considering the cost of transportation to the other side of the world it seemed a good idea and on the 31st July 1952 a royalty agreement was signed which enabled them to commence manufacture and sales for which they would pay an agreed amount per machine.

The Mk 2 broadcaster joined the product list in

The 1951 Mk 1 trailed broadcaster

1953 and was a complete redesign of the previous version. The machine proved so popular that demand exceeded production capacity and components had to be outsourced. About 14,000 of these machines were produced with little competition from other manufacturers. But then, at one of the Royal Smithfield Shows, 17 other machines appeared. Two of them were actually fitted with Teagle castings still with the part numbers! Well, they do say that imitation is the sincerest form of flattery.

The Mk 2 Trailed broadcaster

The 2B LoBin (belt driven) mounted broadcaster

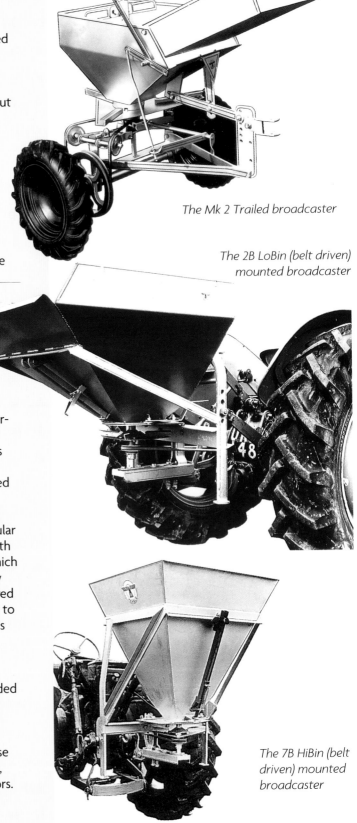

In 1957, the designers came up with the world's first three-point linkage, tractor-mounted PTO-driven broadcaster. The machines were initially belt-driven. Two models were produced at that time, the Lo-Bin, designed for easy loading but only suitable for granular fertilizer, and the HiBin with its steep-sided hopper which could be used for virtually any material from powdered phosphates and basic slag to granular phosphates, seeds and grain.

The manufacturing programme for 1956 included up to 500 broadcasters a month for the UK market – a considerable output. They were designed for use on David Brown, Ferguson, Fordson or Nuffield tractors.

The 7B HiBin (belt driven) mounted broadcaster

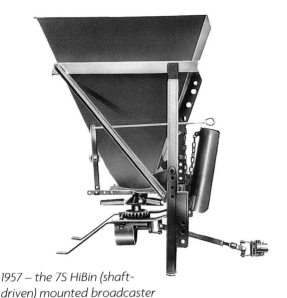

1957 – the 7S HiBin (shaft-driven) mounted broadcaster

The 1961 Versatile mounted broadcaster

The Versatile mounted broadcaster system arc control

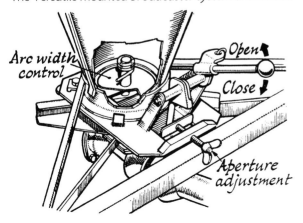

The Versatile broadcaster was hugely important to the company. It was launched at the 1960 Royal Smithfield Show and within three years, production had approached 10,000 machines per year. It became the longest-running model in the range and even in the 1990s was still selling worldwide.

Described at the time as "the most efficient broadcaster made," the Versatile was a revolution in the design of fertilizer spreading machinery. It was fully mounted and the drive to the rotor as the leaflet describes, "has precision cut and hardened bevel gears running in a totally enclosed oil bath gearbox". The hopper and on later machines, the arc control assembly could be completely removed for cleaning "without the use of tools". The patented "arc control" spreading mechanism ensured that no fertilizer was deposited onto the tractor, and the aperture control was adjusted with a stainless steel screw. Comprehensive sowing charts were provided with every machine.

The Versatile broadcaster was the first machine to promote the overlap system of sowing fertilizers, where the driver spreads to his last wheel mark. This gave easy control of bout width and ensured an even spread over the crop.

The leaflet goes on to say "The Teagle feed system is the only one that spreads 180° backwards irrespective of material being sown – and the only one to spread evenly all common fertilizers and farm seeds – from fish manure to grass seeds". And all this for a retail price of £33! No wonder they sold so well.

Transportation was always a consideration and the design team were tasked with designing a machine which could be stacked so as to occupy as little space as possible. They rose to the task and came up with a design which made it possible to pack 200 Versatile broadcasters into a 40-foot export container without the need to strip them down. The tapered hoppers were placed one inside the other and the frames easily stacked together. Although it was an inexpensive machine, no short cuts were taken and it turned out to be exactly what the farmer wanted and at the right price.

The 1966 Versatile mounted broadcaster

The 1966 Model 1200 mounted broadcaster with steel hopper

1970 – PRL 161G ready to depart with a load of 200 Versatile broadcasters

1971 – Versatile broadcaster with plastic hopper

In 2010 Mike Stephens of Western Australia sent a photograph of an elderly, but still working, Versatile broadcaster with a steel hopper. Unfortunately the serial number was missing but his guess that it was made sometime between 1950 and 1960 turned out to be very near the mark. Mike had emigrated in 1966 for £10 but recalled his farming days in Cornwall when he visited the Teagle factory with Landrake Young Farmers Club.

There were many modifications to the broadcasters over the years but a big change came in 1971 when the hoppers were formed in moulded polyethylene. The material had many advantages: it was flexible, easily moulded and lightweight, would not rot or rust and was reasonably resistant to UV light damage. Initially, it was used on the Versatile and 1200 broadcasters and, in time, it became a standard feature on the entire range. Although the supply of the moulded hoppers was subcontracted, Tom Teagle made sure that he fully understood the process by visiting the suppliers to learn how to work with plastics.

1971 – Model 1200 broadcaster with plastic hopper.

The first twin-rotor broadcaster, the Elite, was belt-driven and designed around a frame carrying two spreader mechanisms under two separate hoppers. Each rotor covered the full width of spread, ensuring super-accurate distribution of all types of materials.

The production life of the broadcasters was considerable and, in 1983, the AT range was developed from the Elite model. This range had a single hopper feeding two rotors. Other changes were related to the increased load capacity of tractors. which made it possible to produce larger broadcasters of over one-and-a-half-ton capacity.

The XT range was launched in 1991 to suit farms ranging from low to high acreage. There was a greater use of stainless steel in the spreading mechanism and the extensive use of steel pressings provided a mainframe of great strength for a relatively

1977 – The Elite broadcaster

1984 – The AT 44 mounted broadcaster

light weight. The range was further extended in 1996 with the introduction of the TD50 broadcaster. This machine, with a capacity of up to two tonnes, was fitted with a new gearbox and arc control system.

A 1986 brochure

Teagle Spreaders

My choice for Accuracy and Reliability

1985 – *The AT 18 mounted broadcaster*

1987 – *The AT 44 mounted broadcaster*

1991 – The XT22 mounted broadcaster

1991 – The XT46 mounted broadcaster

1996 – The TD50 mounted broadcaster

The XT24 and XT48 broadcasters appeared in 2004. With a new range of hoppers and an increased carrying capacity, the shape of the machine completely changed. Also upgraded after 43 years, with a new main frame and gearbox, was the Versatile. Now renamed the Compact 8, it still kept its familiar plastic hopper.

The Top-line S60 fertilizer broadcaster was first produced in 2001 and made its debut at the Royal Show the following year. It was an improvement on the TD50 and had a stainless steel hopper to increase its resistance to fertilizers. It is shown here with the Telescopic Big Bag Lifter which made the loading of mounted broadcasters a one-man job .

2004 – The Compact 8, the latest incarnation of the Versatile broadcaster

2004 – The XT48 mounted broadcaster

During the early years the company's machines were displayed at many shows but always on distributors' stands. In 1951, however, it was decided to increase the profile and Teagles took its own stand. Fittingly, for this very Cornish company, it was at the Royal Cornwall Show at Newquay and it must have been with some pride that the company's machines were exhibited to such a large audience.

Tom set out on his first export trip in 1951, to Germany, and over the next twenty years or so he made many such trips. Some were just across the channel to France, Belgium and Holland but as the company's tentacles began to reach out he also found himself in Australia, Switzerland, Canada, the USA and Iceland. On occasions he was accompanied by Mary on business trips which were their only "holidays".

Gerald Blackney began working for Teagles in 1952, when there were only about 25 on the payroll. During the ten years that he worked there the number increased to 120 but then dropped back again to about 80. For many people, getting to work in those days was not easy. At first, Gerald rode a motorbike and when he arrived on the first day he was told that he could leave it in a shed across the yard. He said, "I took it down there and suddenly I was face to face with this huge shire horse. Luckily for me it didn't seem to mind sharing its home. There were many of the old farm buildings still in use then including an old farm labourer's cottage which was our canteen."

Not many of the men had cars and to avoid this being a barrier the company provided Gerald with a van to "bus" people in from the Redruth and Camborne area. Gradually, though, more and more employees had their own "wheels" and the van was no longer needed. Gerald said, "There was often a bit of horseplay in the van and on one occasion it was so boisterous that we almost turned over. Luckily Mr Teagle didn't get to hear about it".

The Jetcut Hedge-Trimmer
and its 49cc engine

1952 – The prototype Jetcut with a Trojan Engine

The first Jetcut hedge-trimmer leaflet

Hedge-trimming was a laborious task. Hedgerows need to be trimmed but, when done by hand, involved hours of work which could be better spent on more productive activity. Anything that could save time and divert manpower to producing food was worth pursuing.

A hand-held mechanical trimmer was the Holy Grail but finding a light enough engine proved difficult. The early prototype was fitted with a Trojan engine, but being made of cast iron, it proved to be too heavy to use for long periods.

Finally, in desperation, Tom Teagle, this farmer cum self-taught engineer, decided that if he could not find a suitable engine then he would build his own. So, with no experience of precision engineering, he designed and manufactured a blower-cooled 49cc two-stroke with almost every part produced in-house. It was a totally novel design incorporating an overhung crankshaft with the flywheel magneto supported on an outrigger bearing housing. The crankshaft ran on ball bearings, the big end was a needle roller bearing with the only plain bearing being the small end. The piston moved in a centrifugally cast iron liner shrunk into the aluminium one-piece cylinder and crankcase. There were no gaskets as the aluminium cylinder head was pulled down onto the cylinder liner creating a perfect seal.

Pressure diecast aluminium engine components were used

to keep the weight down –
they were made by High Duty
Alloy (HDA) of Slough. A special
transfer machining line was
designed by a local company to
bore the cylinder and bearing
housings, machine the ports
and drill and tap 18 holes – a
process which was done in less
than five minutes.

1953 – The 49cc two-stroke engine

Ken Crago worked in the
Napier Engine Company
drawing office in the late
years of the Second World
War and, when the conflict
ended, he returned to the
family farm at St Pinnock,
near Liskeard. He joined the
company when it desperately
needed a draughtsman/
designer to complete the
drawings of the castings of
the engine block and cylinder
head.

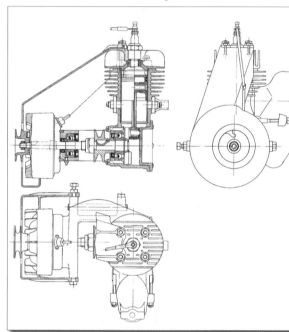

One aspect that attracted
Gerald Blackney to the
company was his interest in
engines and much of his time
there was spent in building
them. Gerald's uncle was a
land agent for the Williams
family and he contacted the
company to ask whether
there was any chance of a
job. Following this, Gerald
was told to go out to see Mr
Teagle. Gerald said, "I went to
the factory one dark winter's
night and found him in the
workshop trying to repair a
grinding machine. He asked
me a few questions and then
told me to start the following
Monday."

It was in the depth of winter
and bitterly cold when Gerald
started but conditions at the

*1953 – This early chain-drive Jetcut
hedge-trimmer fitted with the
Teagle 49cc engine proved to be
popular and a forerunner of all
similar machines
across the world.
It sold well and
was exported
to Japan, India,
New Zealand
and across
Europe.*

1953 – Tom Teagle demonstrating an early Jetcut

The 1954 Jetcut leaflet

factory were considerably better than when the business started. He said, "My father was an apprentice carpenter with Sampson, the builder, during the mid-1920s. Their workshop was at the top of Blackwater Hill and they were hired to erect the Dutch barn at Tywarnhayle Farm. It was the same barn which was later to become one of the machine shops where I worked. Before I started, the men were only protected from the elements by tarpaulins draped around the outside of the building but by the time that I arrived they'd been replaced by a single-skin of galvanised corrugated sheeting. It wasn't ideal – it did help to protect us from the worst of the wind but it was still very cold."

Tom did not want people to think that the engines were untried and untested so the numbering began at 4,000. When Gerald Blackney left, in 1962, it was somewhere around 23,000.

The engines were used on a variety of machines and, according to the paper *Cornish Creativity* in 1985, more than 30,000 left the factory during the ten-year production period.

Many years later, an elderly Teagle two-stroke 49cc engine was the cause of some excitement to Philip Bradbury who discovered it when he paused to talk to a lady who had an old Jetscythe. The machine was beyond repair but the engine intrigued him and when he showed some interest in it she told him that he could have it. It required a fair amount of tender love and affection, not to mention a few new parts, and after making contact he was able to get it working again. It then had a second life – powering a lighting-set at rallies. The story appeared in the March 1985 edition of the magazine *Stationary Engines* and alongside it was an article by Kenneth Crago who had been the engine designer at Teagles from about 1953. He said that many thousands of this type of engine were produced at a rate of just over 100 per day.

This New Year's card cleverly conveyed the message that there was always a better way

Teagle's Rowe Hillmaster lorry was manufactured by a small firm based at Dobwalls, near Liskeard. This early 1955 photograph shows the sign over the cab which reads, "Another load of Teagle Jetcut for Export"

The Jetcut was not popular with everyone and has been described by one writer as an unpleasant machine to use. It was a trail-blazer, however, and one of the first successful self-contained hand-held mechanical hedge-trimmers. One disgruntled user described it as a machine which was worn rather than carried due to the fact that it was slung across the back and left shoulder and supported by a stout leather strap. Despite his memory of it he did include it in his collection of old machines so perhaps he had warmed to it during the intervening years.

1958 – The shaft drive Jetcut with open gears

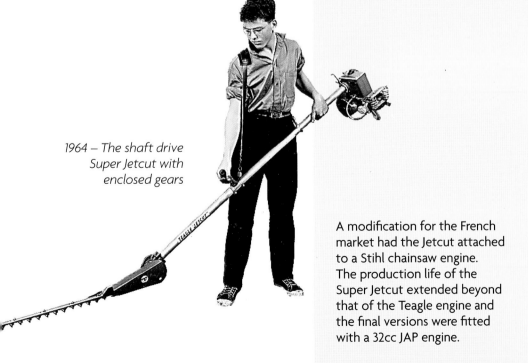

1964 – The shaft drive Super Jetcut with enclosed gears

A modification for the French market had the Jetcut attached to a Stihl chainsaw engine. The production life of the Super Jetcut extended beyond that of the Teagle engine and the final versions were fitted with a 32cc JAP engine.

Other uses for the 49cc engine

The need for a lightweight engine for the hand-held hedge-trimmer was undoubtedly the reason for the production of the 49cc two-stroke engine but it was not the only piece of equipment to use this remarkable little product. During its lifetime it was fitted to a wide variety of machines. One of these was the 1953 cyclemotor, a device designed to remove the hard work of pedalling up Cornish hills. The intention was to reduce the amount of muscle-power needed rather than to remove it altogether. It was also a boon to those who liked to travel that little bit further.

1956 – The Teagle model C Cyclemotor

It was said that Norman Dell of Mount Hawke was a "test pilot" for the machine. Apparently he rode a motorised bicycle and was such a good advertisement for it that the company did not charge him for any replacements.

The cyclemotor was a clip-on power unit for fitting to conventional bicycles. The propulsion was through a friction roller driving on the rear tyre. There was also a 12-volt lighting supply and air cooling as standard (presumably for the engine rather than the rider!) Russell Fowler said that it

The 1964 Jetscythe with the two-stroke engine

The Jetiller was a single wheel horticultural tractor, ideal for rowcrop work – shown here splitting potato banks.

The 1957 Jettiller

The Jetiller – just one of the machines which were a boon to Cornish horticulturists

SPEEDIER CULTIVATIONS AND HOEING

—with the handy

TEAGLE
Jetiller
MONO WHEEL TRACTOR

THE SIGN OF EFFICIENCY

SAVES TIME MANPOWER AND MONEY

"worked proper" but with the driving mechanism positioned against the wheel the friction reduced the life of the tyre.

It is interesting to note that the company offered a service exchange engine for the price of £4 10s 0d. The unit was light enough to be posted to the factory and was completely reconditioned and returned to the customer the same day. Many years later, in 1999, the engine was the subject of a story in *The Vintage Motor Cycle* under the heading of "Teagle Travel". Dave Roberts, a Cornishman living "upcountry" wrote, "Being a Cornishman I thought that I should have a 'motorcycle' from the principality. The only machine I could think of was the early 1950s Teagle – 49cc Cycle Motor engine."

The one that he found needed a considerable amount of work to bring it back to working condition but with the help of a few spare parts, including some items robbed from an old lawn mower, he was mobile. In 1977 he tested it by taking part in the Pioneer Run to Brighton and then joined the Bristol to Lands End run for a return to his birthplace. It was a long haul and his mention of entering a pub in Fowey smelling like the Cornish scrum after a wet game is descriptive rather than attractive. Anyway, he did it and this quote is a short account of his very interesting and amusing story.

The Jetscythe was not a huge success but this seems to have been due to the lack of a sales force at that time rather than any inadequacy in the machine itself. In 2007, one was discovered in the back of a barn in north Scotland. It was in reasonable condition but a little work was necessary to coax it back to life.

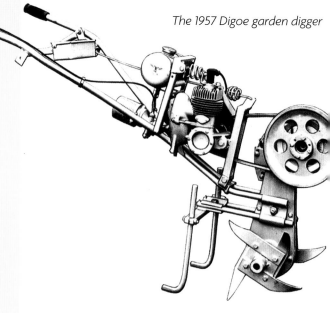

The 1957 Digoe garden digger

The 1956 lawn mower shown here being used by Mary Teagle. An interesting photograph with Tom's Teagle's mother in the background and his Armstrong Siddeley, JDR 1

Ship Ahoy! at St Ives – this 1956 photograph of four lads enjoying themselves at St Ives did have a serious point to it. The boat was powered and steered by a 49cc Teagle engine and a young Fred Teagle seems to be in control of the situation. It was a prototype and did not reach the production stage but the impression is that it certainly seemed to do the trick.

Other Engines

It seemed a natural progression to add a four-stroke engine to the range but before work could start it was necessary to create some additional space and to acquire new machinery. As with the two-stroke version, it was difficult to find a good-quality lightweight engine, and that was the motivation for making these, necessity being the mother of invention. They were originally used on the elevators but later were also fitted to the Jettillers and Jetscythes. The product sheet claims that this engine was probably the only one in its class to be fitted with just one plain bearing throughout – the small end bearing. All other bearings were either ball or needle rollers.

1958 – The 126cc four-stroke engine

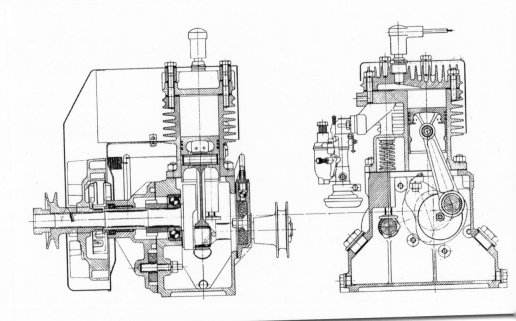

1959 – Designer Ken Crago operating the
Jetiller with rotary cultivator attachment
fitted with a Teagle four-stroke engine

*The last model of the
Jetscythe – with a Briggs
and Stratton engine*

At times you get the impression that part of the challenge for Tom Teagle was how to make a machine that was different. The exhaust and inlet ports were close together, with the inlet port being sufficiently long to act as a vaporiser so the engine could run on TVO (Tractor Vaporising Oil). The engine was governed, it had oil pump lubrication and a unique half-speed reduction output which could be taken from the end of its massive camshaft. It was designed, tooled and manufactured in under eight months but its production life was only six years. By then, cheaper engines were available from America, and Briggs and Stratton engines were used on elevators from 1964 and on Jetillers and Jetscythes from 1965.

Before we leave the subject of engines we should mention that a diesel engine was also produced. Unfortunately it did not progress beyond the prototype stage and Dick Littlejohns recalled the engine and additional parts being stored in the old granary for many years.

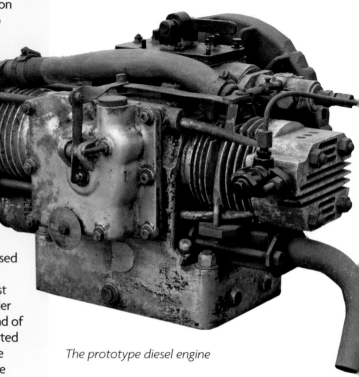

This novel diesel engine was a 126cc horizontal two-stroke with a compressor cylinder opposed to the power cylinder. This compressor blew the exhaust gases from the power cylinder as the piston reached the end of its stroke. The engine was fitted with a governor and pressure lubrication and as with all the other Teagle engines, the only plain bearings were the small ends.

The prototype diesel engine

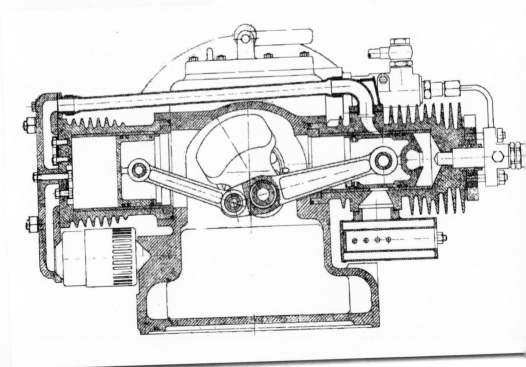

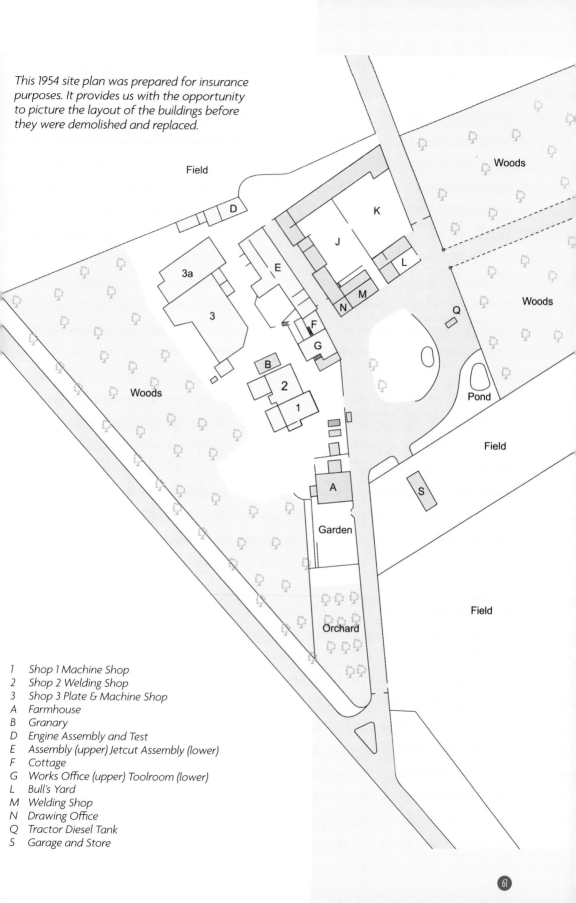

This 1954 site plan was prepared for insurance purposes. It provides us with the opportunity to picture the layout of the buildings before they were demolished and replaced.

Field

Woods

D

K

J

3a

E

L

3

M

N

F

Q

Woods

G

B

2

Woods

1

Pond

Field

A

S

Garden

Field

Orchard

1   Shop 1 Machine Shop
2   Shop 2 Welding Shop
3   Shop 3 Plate & Machine Shop
A   Farmhouse
B   Granary
D   Engine Assembly and Test
E   Assembly (upper) Jetcut Assembly (lower)
F   Cottage
G   Works Office (upper) Toolroom (lower)
L   Bull's Yard
M   Welding Shop
N   Drawing Office
Q   Tractor Diesel Tank
S   Garage and Store

Tom Teagle was in Lincolnshire, demonstrating one of his machines. After breakfast he left the hotel and jumped into his Armstrong Siddeley. He must have thought it a bit strange that so many people were waving to him and it was not until he reached the end of the road that he discovered the reason. Another driver wound down his window and told him that he had just driven down a one-way street. Tom's reaction: "Well, what of it?"

Outside of work, Tom did not seem to have many interests but one or two people have said that he did enjoy watching wrestling on the television. If he was working with someone on a Saturday morning, it was not unusual for him to leave them to it while he disappeared into the house to watch a bit of Kent Walton and the grunt and groan boys.

Most of the workshops were originally farm buildings. They were primitive by today's standards with little chance of maintaining a reasonable working temperature. Heating often comprised a five-gallon drum filled with coke which, when it was glowing red, was carried into the workplace. It helped to take the chill off the winter mornings but, more often than not, produced clouds and clouds of smoke.

By 1954 rationing had come to an end and 14 years of restrictions on the sale and purchase of meat and many other items were lifted. The then Minister of Fuel and Power, Geoffrey Lloyd, celebrated by burning a large replica of a ration book and the Minister of Food, Major Gwilym Lloyd-George, told a meeting in Cheshire that he would keep his as a souvenir. He praised all those traders and organisations that had co-operated with the rationing system. They were difficult times but great efforts were made to ensure that Britain could feed itself. Perhaps now, in 2015, we have lost sight of that necessity.

John Veall joined the company in January 1954, straight from school. He walked into the yard and asked a man working there, where he could find Mr Teagle. The response he received was a little unexpected: "It's me, what do you want?" John told him that he was looking for a job and, following a few questions about who he was and where he was from, he was told, "Start Monday". Perhaps the answer that he was a farmer's son was the deciding factor as Tom Teagle set great store by the skills of these multi-skilled sons of the soil. Ironically, many years previously, John's grandfather had declined an offer to rent Tywarnhayle Farm from the Williams family as he felt that taking on such a large unit was too big a gamble.

At the time there were about 70 men on the payroll, some on the farm and others in the factory, working on a product range which included artificial fertilizer broadcasters, engines and concrete mixers. Much of the material was delivered by road but rail was still an important mode of transport for the company. It was not unusual for a GWR (Great Western Railway or, if you prefer, God's Wonderful Railway) lorry to turn up with a load. Of course, back then, there were no fork lift trucks and everything had to be unloaded by hand.

Gerald Blackney recalled making some gates for the Hawke family, Mrs Teagle's relatives. When the gates were finished they were dipped in hot tar to prevent them from rusting. The tar was in a shallow tank about 14 feet long. It was heated by paraffin burners and, when the tar was sufficiently molten, two men, one at each end, dropped the gates into the black liquid. Gerald said, "Back then, we were always on the lookout for a bit of fun, it was what created the camaraderie. I remember that whoever was the stronger of the two men would give a tug to try to get the other man to step into the tar tank. It was the reason that we always wore rubber boots for that job. There was very little thought given to health and safety in those days but we put our heart and soul into the job – and our muscles."

The
Elevators

The prototype multi-level elevator

1954 – The later production multi-level elevator

As the farming world progressed from sheaves to bales there was very little change in handling the hay and straw. It was all done by hand and after a day spent throwing bales to the top of a growing pile, knocking-off time never seemed to arrive soon enough. Teagles was not the first company to make elevators but Tom had a few ideas about how the existing versions could be improved and he soon began to produce them, complete with his own enhancements.

Tom watched as a man on a wagon threw a bale down onto the ground. A second man then picked it up and placed it on the elevator where it was taken to the top of the rick. This double-handling must have irritated him but it was the inspiration for the world's first multi-level bale elevator. With this innovation, the lower end of the conveyor could be raised or lowered to enable bales to be placed onto it, direct from the wagon.

The next aspect to grab his attention was out in the field where the workers were spending long hours carrying out the seemingly unnecessary back-breaking job of loading bales onto trailers and lorries. The design team was set to work and the result was an elevator with guides to deflect the bales onto the conveyor as it was driven along. It was then possible to pick up the bales automatically and deliver

1959 – The Major C elevator

them to the top of the load. Once again, one of their products had resulted in a major saving on labour. Two versions were produced, the Zup, a complete multilevel elevator, and the Speediloader, an automatic pick-up version.

The elevators were a bit ungainly to move and Fred Teagle remembers towing three of them in convoy with a single tractor. He said, "They were difficult to keep in a straight line and we snaked our way down Blackwater Hill on our way to Chacewater Station".

The February 1963 price shows that you could buy a bale elevator for just £115 including delivery to your nearest railway station. The company's telephone number at that time was Threewaters 242 but that was long before the area came under the Truro telephone exchange.

1958 – The Zup automatic pick-up elevator

1961 – The Speediloader

The elevators were a good line at this time and during the period May to July, over 430 left the factory gate. No doubt, most were destined for use on farms but they were useful machines and with a bit of lateral thinking they could be put to a variety of non-agricultural uses including raising concrete blocks on building sites.

The Tumbleloader was a progression from the

original automatic pick-up elevator. The main difference was the special high-sided trailer which collected the bales and tipped them out at the rick. The trailer was fitted with a hitch which automatically connected and disconnected the elevator which could remain in the field while the trailer was being unloaded.

The Ranger elevator was then used to deliver the bales onto the rick. A feature of the elevator was that it could be controlled by the man at the top of the rick who could swivel the machine to deliver the bales exactly where needed.

1960 – A batch of elevators waiting for the train at Chacewater Station

1974 – The Tumbleloader and trailer

1977 – The Ranger bale elevator

A conveyance dated the 10th December 1954 confirms that Tywarnhayle Farm had, at last, passed into the ownership of the Teagle family. It was signed by The Right Honourable Charles Williams, Member of Parliament and Privy Councillor, of Caerhays Castle, Gorran, near St Austell, the vendor, and by Tom Teagle on behalf of W T Teagle (Machinery) Ltd. It included the farm complex and the land and plantations on both sides of the Truro to St Agnes road. The family had rented the farm for 41 years but now it was finally theirs.

With the war a distant memory, home-produced food was becoming more plentiful and could be purchased at a reasonable price. There was, however, a new threat on the horizon. Farm hands were aware of the dry and comfortable conditions enjoyed by factory workers and, despite the advances in technology, farming was still hard work. The pay for farm workers was also lower than could be earned elsewhere and soon many began to leave the land. The imperative now was to make better use of the remaining workforce, to make farming a less labour-intensive industry – to embrace mechanisation. In this respect the farming industry was beginning to catch up with Tom Teagle's way of thinking. From the early beginnings, his message had been that there had to be a better way. If greater output was to be achieved then the future lay in mechanisation, to make the industry less dependent on the need for more and more manpower.

A clear sign that the family's future lay in manufacture was the sale of most of the farmland. In 1955, a large portion of the land, mainly to the east of the little river that meanders down to Jericho Valley and on to Trevellas Beach, was sold to Mr and Mrs Noel Hoskins of Greenacres Farm, Silverwell. About seven years later, the fields on both sides of the Truro to St Agnes road were sold. Some were added to Greenacres Farm while the remainder, including those to the west of the road, were purchased by Leatham Farms Ltd. Later, in the early 1970s, further individual fields were sold but this was more a tidying-up process, leaving the company with sufficient area for its future needs. This final disposal cut the direct ties with agriculture production – the future for Tom Teagle and his family was then firmly in the manufacture of agricultural machinery.

Gerald Blackney almost shivered as he recalled how cold the factory was at times. He said, "You had a thin sheet of corrugated steel between you and the north wind. On one occasion I was working at the far end of the building, at the opposite end to the generators, when Mr Teagle came over and asked if I could feel the difference. I didn't know what he meant and told him so. I think that he was a bit irritated that I wasn't more appreciative but all he had done was to remove the galvanised sheets between the generator and the workshop. He reckoned that it was much warmer. I told him that I couldn't notice the difference and he proceeded to lecture me about wearing too many layers of clothing. 'The trouble is,' he said, 'the heat can't get through'."

In the summer, Tom wore very little, if anything, under his boiler suit ("commando fashion"). This was very clear on an occasion when he was bending over laying pipes and the crotch of his boiler suit was long overdue for the darning needle. In discussing that particular area of his anatomy, another story springs to mind – one which could have had a more serious result. He was fully occupied in welding and was quite unconcerned at the large rip in the front of his overalls. It must have been a bit warm but he soldiered on and it was not until a little later that he discovered that he was extremely "sun-burnt" in an area where he shouldn't be!

When working on an idea Tom Teagle would often ask someone to make a component part but his instructions would often come in the form of hand semaphore: he would indicate the shape with his arm or hand before sending the person off to make it. Gerald Blackney said that nine times out of ten it fitted the bill. but when Tom was talking to someone who was relatively new then the instruction did not always fully sink in. On one occasion he gave his usual visual description and the man went off to make the part but as he was passing the scrap pile he saw an item which looked something like it. After a few minutes he took it back and Mr Teagle said, "That didn't take long, I want another hundred". Another favourite of his was to draw the shape on the concrete floor with a piece of chalk but, unless the piece was made immediately, the poor chap could easily find that someone had "accidently" rubbed it out with his shoe. Russell Fowler recalled the occasion when Tom Teagle asked him to make a bicycle rack. He said, "I decided to make it in the cottage. After I had welded it up I realised that it was too big to get out through the door. I tried all ways but in the end I had to give up and cut it into pieces and re-weld it outside. I don't think that Mr Teagle knew but after all that it was never used."

Outsourcing components has its risks and delivery times can sometimes be jeopardised when suppliers fail to deliver on time. One such occasion involved a consignment of wheels. John Veall said, "We had 120 broadcasters lined up in the drive all waiting for wheels. When they eventually arrived there was a mad rush to fit them and then get them down to Chacewater Railway Station. From there they were sent all over the country."

Chacewater Station was essential to the company at this time and when I was interviewing former employee Claude Tonkin for another book he recalled Tom Teagle telling him to drive the tractor and trailer there to pick up some parts. Claude protested that he did not have a driving licence but Tom sent him anyway.

Like most of the other men, John Veall cycled to work and for him this meant a five and a half-mile journey from Gwennap Pit. He was mainly involved on the engineering side but, when the need arose, he and his colleagues had to help on the farm. On one occasion all hands were needed to carry the hay so most of the men jumped on their bikes and cycled to the field. The chance of a ride back was attractive so the bicycles were placed on the forks of the stacker and off they set. Unfortunately someone tripped the forks as they were heading back to the farm and in an instant the tractor had crunched its way over the precious load of bicycles.

Bad weather was no barrier to reaching work and on one occasion John Veall set off with about one foot of snow on the ground. He said, "I walked most of the way and reached there by about ten o'clock. When I arrived I was told that there was no point being there and that I may as well go home again."

A book by Brian Bell entitled *Fifty Years of Garden Machinery*, for machinery enthusiasts and collectors, featured the small machines manufactured by Teagles – the ones which took the drudgery out of work in market gardens and smallholdings. It talked of engineering ingenuity and quoted the Jetscythe as an example of a power-driven single-wheel machine with a cutter bar which coped with grass and weeds in gardens and orchards. The engine-driven Jetcut, lawn mowers and cultivators were all included.

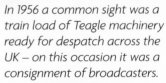

In 1956 a common sight was a train load of Teagle machinery ready for despatch across the UK – on this occasion it was a consignment of broadcasters.

The Loader-Stacker that did the damage.

1958 – The prototype Tracut mounted hedge-trimmer

The Tractor-Mounted Hedge-Trimmers

Necessity is the mother of invention and with good farm workers becoming increasingly difficult to find there was a growing need to mechanise and let the tractor take the strain.

Hedge-trimming had moved from the man with a hook to the Jetcut but this still depended on a person walking the perimeter of the field. It would be good if this machine, or one adapted from it, could be tractor-mounted. In 1957 the design team's ingenuity was brought to bear on the issue, the following year the problems had been cracked. The resultant machine, the Tracut, was designed with a simple lifting mechanism using the tractor lift arms. It worked well and another tedious aspect of farm work had been mechanised.

The Silver Bullet Tracut, was first produced in 1962 as a rear-mounted hedge-trimmer with fingertip head-angling. France proved to be a highly successful market with up to 60 machines a week being exported there.

1958 – The Tracut mounted hedge-trimmer

1962 – The Tracut Silver Bullet mounted hedge-trimmer

Next came the Tracut Golden Bullet, in which the main driving pulley was replaced by a gearbox, which gave the machine a much neater appearance and reduced the likelihood of damage in transit.

In September 1966 both the *Western Morning News* and the *West Briton* included stories about the company's deliveries to France. "*On Monday night Mr Selwood Magor climbed into the cabin of his articulated Ford lorry with the homely Cornish number-plate FCV 224D and within 24 hours he was approaching the outskirts of Paris. It was a door-to-door delivery service which compared with the earlier arrangement of almost four weeks.*"

The journey, which included a crossing on the new ferry service from Southampton to Le Havre, was a regular run – in the height of the season it was made three times in a fortnight. The decision to use in-house transport was taken because of delays and damage during the previous shipping

1962 – Fred Teagle demonstrating the mid-mounted Tracut Silver Bullet hedge-trimmer.

1964 – Cyril Kent using the Tracut Golden Bullet hedge-trimmer

1966 – Selwood Magor of Redruth about to leave on the Paris run with 70 Tracut Golden Bullet hedge-trimmers on board

arrangements. Teagles had worked hard to capture a large share of the French market and had no intention of losing it because of poor performance by outside hauliers.

In 1975 the Tracut gave way to the Dynacut, a new flail hedge-trimmer. The huge advantage of the new model was its ability to mulch the cut material, removing the necessity to collect and remove it – a huge labour-saving feature. The first two models, the 300 and the 400, were designed on the same principle as the Tracut and met with reasonable success but they were difficult to mount onto the tractor. It needed a rethink and a return to the basic idea. The result was a new machine – the Dynacut 400 Mk 2 and Series A. While the former strengthened the sales to France, the Series A was more popular with British farmers. Later, other models followed, including the highly successful Dynacut SBX and the Model K with the parallel linkage boom.

1974 – The Dynacut 400 Mk 1 hedge-trimmer

1975 – The Dynacut 400 Mk 2 hedge-trimmer

1975 – The Dynacut Series A hedge-trimmer

1979 – The Dynacut SBX hedge-trimmer

1980 – The Dynacut K hedge-trimmer

Fred Teagle joined the business in 1957 but by then he had already clocked up many hours of part-time involvement. He worked there during his school holidays and even made an unaccompanied trip to France to demonstrate a hedge-trimmer – when he was just 16. He had inherited a great interest in engineering and it was no surprise when he took his place in the company. He joined with a good appreciation of the various functions and was able to hit the ground running. He soon became involved in demonstrating and selling but his real interest was in making the products and he was soon made production director. Later, when the company had acquired the Tuckingmill site, most of his time was spent there.

In April 1958 Mike Stephens started work at the Blackwater factory. Like other young lads he began by cleaning the workshops and the machines. He soon progressed to the workbench and for many years he worked alongside Denzil Moyle. In 1974 he was made foreman of the fabrication and welding shop. He then managed the assembly shop and, when Bob Fowler retired, he became assistant works manager under John Veall, a position he held until he retired in 2008. Mike was one of a number of men who managed to clock up 50 years of service in the company.

Before the sale of the last few fields there were usually a few head of sheep and cattle to look after and one day, on his way to work, Mike came across a herd on Blackwater Hill. He recognised them as belonging to the farm. When he arrived at the factory he set off to find Tom Teagle who said, "Well, you'd better go back and get them".

"That was the end of the farm," said Mike. "Tom Teagle said that he was far too busy to waste time chasing cattle. Before long they were all gone."

One amusing story from 1958 relates to the rebuilding of shop 6. A clump of trees were in the way and had to go. They were cut down and removed but getting rid of the motts (tree stumps) was more of a problem. In those days there were no hydraulic excavators on hand so, once again, it was to Harry Fowler that they turned. Harry had already dealt with many of the trees beside the road so removing these would be no problem. Luckily, he still held a blasting licence and with the help of a few sticks of dynamite these would soon be out of the way. He began by boring a hole in the centre of one of the stumps. He then dropped in the stick of dynamite, lit the fuse and signalled for everyone to take cover. It was in an open yard with no prospect of anything going wrong. After all, Harry had pronounced, "I can't see any problem". In truth, his confidence was well placed but he had not reckoned on his colleague, Tom James, returning at that very moment. Tom drove his lorry into the yard and parked next to the tree stump – the tree stump with the dynamite in it. Everyone shouted but Tom must have thought that they were just being friendly – he waved back, turned and walked away. The huge explosion must have scared the pants off him but, luckily, he was shielded from the blast and lived to tell the tale.

Another similar story came from Gerald Blackney who recalled Harry's attempts to clear some other tree stumps. He said, "The dynamite was kept in a building which we called the granary, it was a wooden building raised up on staddle stones (granite mushroom supports). Harry had drilled the holes in one tree stump and inserted the dynamite but Tom Teagle wasn't satisfied that he was using enough." Harry seems to have taken the line that if that was what the boss wanted then that was what he was going to get. He added some more and lit the fuse. There was a huge bang and the mott took off, right up in the air. Of course, what goes up must come down and this one did, straight through the barn roof. Gerald said, "I don't think that Tom was a very happy bunny but he had told him to use the extra dynamite so he couldn't blame Harry".

One luckless chap was doing some painting when he managed to put his foot in a bucket of paint. He must have lost his balance because when he tried to extricate himself he upset the contents all over the floor. Unfortunately for him, Tom Teagle saw it happen. He told him to get some paraffin to clean it up. Either the chap was naturally clumsy or the sound of Mr Teagle's voice unnerved him because he somehow managed to upset the paraffin as well.

Shortly after Tom Teagle gave up smoking he introduced a no-smoking policy throughout the works. (They say that there is no one more self-righteous than a reformed smoker!) Perhaps suspecting that it was a ruse to cut down on wasted time, many of the men disliked the new rule and a few carried on regardless, albeit surreptitiously. Perhaps the time spent smoking was at the forefront of Tom's mind but there was also a health and safety reason, the twin risks of personal accident and fire. Few, however, saw it that way and one chap even questioned what could possibly catch fire. Mind you, he was the same person who, many years later, gave up smoking and regretted that he had not done so at the time. Gerald Blackney, a non-smoker, was one of the charge hands who had to enforce the rule. He said, "Some of the men couldn't do without their fags so they would go down to the toilets and light up. I don't know if they thought they couldn't be seen but sometimes there were so many there that you could see the clouds of smoke. Mr Teagle knew what was going on but I suppose he turned a blind eye, after all

they had to go to the toilet. I was one of those who had to go down to get them back to work. There were only four cubicles and to this day I hold the record of turning out the greatest number of men – sixteen." Gerald continued, "On another occasion, Tom spotted a man smoking and was determined to make an example of him. He marched down across the yard so fast that I could hardly keep up. I called after him to say that he couldn't sack him but he shouted back that he was the boss and could sack who he liked. Eventually though I managed to convince him that it wasn't a good idea. The chap was a lorry driver who had just delivered a load of steel."

The rule was also applied at Tuckingmill and on one occasion a welder was having a quiet smoke – at the same time that he was welding. When Fred Teagle walked in he managed to hide the cigarette in his hand but Fred was aware that he was smoking and stayed a bit longer than the chap hoped. It must have become a bit uncomfortable until Fred said, "Cyril, I don't know whether you're on fire but I can see the smoke coming out of your collar".

Another instance involved one of the welders at Blackwater who stood under an extractor, confident that the smoke would be sucked out before anyone could tell that he was having a sly drag. Unfortunately for him, his cigarette was sucked up with the smoke and he suddenly realised that he had set fire to the extraction system. "He didn't do it again!"

Some, perhaps many, referred to Tom Teagle as the "Old Man" but it was not to his face and certainly not within earshot of his wife. If she did overhear it, then they would quickly feel the sharp edge of her tongue. Gerald Blackney said, "She would tell us that it was Mr Teagle but I'm sure that she knew that there was no malice intended. A few of us often worked alongside Tom on the prototypes, sometimes in the evening, and I remember that Mrs Teagle would always bring us down a tray of saffron buns and a jug of hot cocoa, it was always cocoa."

Nicknames aside, Gerald said, "I always got on well with the boss. If you kept your nose clean and did a decent day's work that was all he expected. He was very good about letting us have material if we were making something for ourselves. I was working on an old Austin seven car and wanted some sheet aluminium which he let me have at cost. He didn't even charge me for the nuts and bolts because he reckoned that working out the cost would be more than they were worth. I think that he appreciated me asking rather than just taking them. We used to refer to small jobs done on the side as 'Jan Lukes,' a term that came from Holman's. If you wanted to do anything a bit bigger then Tom didn't mind you using the factory at the weekend. I remember that I was out there one evening working on the car and he came down to give me a hand. When it was finished and on the road he took a look at it and said, 'We did a good job there, didn't we?'"

Potato Harvesting Machinery

1958 – The Spudnick potato harvester

A 1959 Spudnick leaflet

Mary Teagle's family were involved in growing potatoes and it should be no surprise that her husband channelled some of his energies into designing machines to harvest them.

A prototype was produced during 1956/7 and was soon being tested on the family farms in the St Columb area. It easily passed the test and within a year or so the newly named Spudnick took its place at the National Potato Harvesting Demonstration at Beverley, in Yorkshire. It competed successfully with machines needing more man power and costing more than double the price.

Tom's system of naming new products often involved inviting suggestions from friends and acquaintances. He would offer a prize for the suggestion that he liked the best. Employees were excluded but Gerald Blackney does claim the credit for the potato harvester, Spudnick. He said, "The name was introduced about the same time that the Russian Sputnik programme was under way. I took a piece of chalk from my pocket and wrote the name on the side of the prototype and when Tom Teagle spotted it, the Spudnick Potato Harvester was born. I was quite pleased at the time but I'm still waiting for my prize!" He went on to say that one of the problems with the machine was the excessive noise it made. Later models produced by other companies had rubber drive belts but the Spudnick had metal chains and made quite a racket. One day, when Gerald

1962 – The LPD single-row potato digger (1968 photograph)

was walking from the car park to the Royal Cornwall showground, he heard one start up. He said, "Even from there it made quite a din and someone nearby reckoned that it was so noisy that it was only fit for blocking up a gap in a hedge".

In October 1959 the company took its Spudnick potato harvester on the road. It was a long journey to the International Potato Harvester Trials at Southend-on-Sea where its proud boast was that it was the "fastest single row machine on the field". Further shows followed at Dundee, Beverley, Southport and Blackpool. Despite the noise it proved to be a very successful product.

Dick Littlejohns recalled an occasion when Mike Stephens suggested an alteration to the Spudnick which Tom Teagle seemingly ignored. The next morning Tom came down to the workshop and said, "I've been thinking rather extensively about this, you

1962 – The DD two-row potato digger

The Scimitar Potato Haulm Pulveriser

know," and then he came up with exactly the same idea that Mike had suggested.

Despite its obvious success, Tom was still not satisfied that he had achieved the machine's full potential. He was convinced that he could invent some sort of automatic separation system whereby the potatoes could be separated from the earth and stones that were picked up with them. It must have taken quite a bit of head scratching but he finally came up with an idea which comprised a series of suckers mounted above the conveyor belt. The intention was that the individual suckers would lift the potatoes clear for just a second or so while the earth and stones fell back to the ground. Having convinced himself that it would work, a prototype was produced and

1964 – The 7/130 Potato Harvester which was produced in large numbers – the Tuckingmill buildings in the background

soon it was out in the fields being tested. To some extent it worked but problems arose due to the variable nature of the soil, particularly in wet weather. The stickiness made separation inconsistent and the idea was abandoned. From what we are told he was particularly disappointed by this failure and some have even said that he would have died a happy man if he could have found a solution.

Later, the Model 5/120 harvester and the Scimitar haulm pulveriser were added to the range. These machines were light and manoeuvrable which made them ideal for use on smaller tractors. Novel features on the diggers were the reversible driving sprockets, front rollers and agitator sprockets sealed against dirt and the shares and stone traps made from stainless steel. Harvesting is made much easier if the haulm and plant stems are removed prior to digging the crop and this was the motivation for making the pulveriser.

An article in one of the newspapers was headed "Challenge to the Giants" and referred to Teagle's latest potato harvester. **"An ex-farmer who started building machinery as a hobby will be taking on the world's farming machinery giants next month.**

William Teagle of Teagle Machinery designs the agricultural machines that his company turns

May 1966 – A Spudnick Model 7/130 at a demonstration in Australia

1972 - A prototype Two Row Potato Harvester working at the National Demonstration

out. He will take his 7/130 potato harvester to the Potato Marketing Board's harvesters' demonstration in Pembrokeshire on the 15th June and there he will show its capabilities against giants like Massey Ferguson, Grimme Britannia (West Germany), Kromag (West Germany) and Johnson Faun (Norway)."

The company's reputation for producing quality, reliable machines was growing and in 1964 the 7/130 was put to the test. It was taken to the Ripon Potato Harvester Demonstration in Yorkshire where there was no machine that could match it for speed and versatility. As the leaflet said, "Ask any one of the thousands who attended the demonstration!"

The company went on to make and test much larger machines and by the early 1970s were producing large single row and even a prototype two-row machine.

Being based in Cornwall the company was not ideally situated to support the main potato producers in the east of England and Scotland, and competition from continental machines made trading conditions quite difficult. The company's production facilities were not extensive enough to make such large machines and production finally ceased in the mid 1970s, in favour of the manufacture of broadcasters, mixers and hedge-cutters.

Occasionally, there was a minor accident in the factory. Gerald Blackney recalled cutting his thumb which meant a trip to the farmhouse kitchen where Mary Teagle's first aid skills were called into play. Gerald said, "While she was dressing the wound the phone rang. She apologised but said that she had to answer it as it could be an order. When the phone rang for the third time my thumb was still not bandaged. By then, I was feeling a bit faint but business was business and she was certainly an astute business woman." Of course, there was the occasional injury which was beyond her level of competence and there were many journeys to Treliske Hospital Accident and Emergency Department with blood dripping over her car seat. If it happened to coincide with the trip to the post office, so much the better, in which case it was, "You just sit there and bleed while I finish getting the post ready".

On another occasion it must have been one very surprised member of staff who found himself floundering in an open-top dip-tank full of undercoat paint. On this occasion, however, it was the company's adopted moggie which found that its curiosity had almost cost it one of its lives. It scrambled out and scampered away trying to preen its coat back to its former perfection.

Dick Littlejohns was yet another employee who chalked up 50 years with the company. In 1959, he and a friend had ridden their bicycles to the factory and knocked on the front door. Tom Teagle opened it and asked them what they wanted. Dick said that Tom hardly spoke a word – there was no interview or questions. They were just told to start right away. He said, "It was mid-morning on a Saturday and I said that we had to go home first. We actually started on the following Monday." His first 12 months were spent in the maintenance shop with Freddie Bawden from St Agnes. The next move was to production where he worked

for John Hicks making broadcaster hoppers before transferring to the assembly shop where Cyril Kent was in charge. He worked there until he retired in 2011 – three years after his official retirement date.

The
Concrete Mixers

1959 – The Mk 1 Rubber Tyre Drive Tipmix

1960 Tipmix leaflet

The concept of a tractor-mounted concrete mixer created a few problems for the design team but, once they were overcome, the machine was a huge success. It was a must-have item for farmers and probably the world's best-selling tractor-mounted mixer.

The first models were fitted with a roller which drove a rubber tyre mounted on the drum. Unfortunately the rubber tended to wear out quite quickly and later models were fitted with a cast iron gear. The load was tipped using the lifting action of the hydraulic arms.

The early versions of the Tipmix were made to fit specific tractors, with the obvious drawback that it was impossible for agents to hold stocks for every tractor on the market. Some form of standardisation was clearly required and the design team set to work. The result was the Universal Tipmix which was powered by the conventional PTO drive shaft common to most tractors. Unfortunately, this meant that automatic tipping was no longer possible and a change was made to manual tipping. This was done by pulling a projecting arm to tip the load, much like a one-armed bandit.

It was envisaged that the Universal Tipmix would be popular in the overseas markets so great consideration was given to making the mixers compact and easily transportable. The result was that up to 60 machines could be packed into a 40 foot long container and 70 onto a 40 foot long lorry. The Republic of Ireland proved to be an excellent market for these amazing machines and during their life-cycle more than 12,000 were sold there. Similar quantities were delivered to France.

The 1962 Tipmix with the cast gear drive

1966 – The Universal Tipmix

1969 – A load of Tipmix bound for Ireland

December 1979 – ready for the off – David Madge, Transport Manager, preparing to despatch a load of Tipmix to France

A container-load of Tipmix bound for Australia

The Spiromix was the next generation of mixer. It incorporated a different discharge feature – a mechanical reverse drive mechanism which enabled it to unload like a ready-mix lorry. The later Spiromix had a hydraulic reverse mechanism so that the mortar or concrete could be augered out as and where required. Larger models were produced, with the limiting factor being the weight that the tractor could carry. Later, the Spiromix 200F was designed to be fitted onto the forks of telescopic handlers and fork-lifts so that the payload could be delivered to whatever height was required.

The 1979 Spiromix 100 PTO drive mixer

1991 – The Spiromix 200F

Teagles gifted this Spiromix to Zambia where it was used in the construction of a hydro-electric plant – since 2006 this machine has mixed many thousands of cubic metres of concrete with zero faults

The dam – no doubt the Spiromix had some help!

The 1960s

John Veall recalled some of the trips to agricultural shows including the Bath & West at Liskeard, when the company hired a coach to transport those who wanted to attend. "There were others," he said, "including a demonstration trip 'upcountry'. At the end of the day we were all waiting to be served in a bar when Mr Teagle walked in. He tried to attract the barman's attention but there was quite a queue and he was busy. I don't think that he enjoyed standing in a bar and he reached up to a metal advertisement and tried to turn it towards the barman to indicate what he wanted. It wouldn't turn so he bent it around and told him to give us all one of them. He then straightened it and walked out."

Brian Hutchins joined the company in May 1961 and remained until he retired in 2011. He began life in the machine shop where he spent about six months punching and drilling metal...and cleaning the toilets! It was a job reserved for the "boys" and, in his words, he hated it. Toilet duty was carried out at the end of the day and was shared by all new recruits. Brian soon moved to the sheet metal shop, Shop 6, where he worked under John Hicks. During his 15 years there he gained a good insight into life at Teagles. He worked with Harry Strutt on the galvanised hoppers for the Versatile broadcasters – during the winter months they were despatching 250 a week – and with Frank Barr on the mixer drums when production was running at 200 per week. During the summer months many different products were made including the Tracut sectional hedge-trimmer knives which were an important part of the production programme.

Brian's next job, during the early 1980s, was in the welding shop where he worked on the big trailers and the welding jigs for the round bale shredders which were soon to come on stream. He spent 11 years there before being made foreman of Shop 1, in charge of the plasma cutters, CNC presses and the hydraulic ram assembly.

Ron Hendry recalled an occasion when he managed to weld his work to the jig. He said, "I made a proper job and just couldn't separate it. Before I realised what was happening there was a row of about 20 blokes outside my welding bay. Russell Fowler had told them what I'd done and they were queued up to take a look."

During the life of the company there have been many technological changes which have had far-reaching consequences. The use of plastics for items like fertilizer hoppers was just one example. It led to a reduced demand on the sheet metal shop, to such an extent that its activity was transferred to Shop 1. There was, and still is, an ever-present need to be alert to these and other changes, not least the whims of politicians both at home and in Brussels.

Just in case we have failed to convey the picture of Teagles as a major producer, the figure of 2,579 machines sold in the half-year to September 1961 may focus the mind. This was in addition to conversions, overhauls and the sale of spares and associated equipment. The main lines included broadcasters, mixers, the Jetcut and Tracut hedge-trimmers and elevators but there were 15 other products on the list. The turnover, however, was down on the level achieved in 1954. To some extent this was because of the considerable amount of experimental work being undertaken but there was also a growing realisation that the business had become too large to be managed by just Tom and his wife. Since its incorporation, in 1943, they

1960 – The earliest aerial photograph of the works. The various buildings can be identified by reference to the annotated site plan. Comparison of the 1945 site plan with this 1960 version shows how the Blackwater factory site had evolved.

had run the entire business but, in an increasingly competitive world, a broader management structure was required. High on the priority list was better financial control but improved production facilities were also urgently needed. The latter prompted an interest in the old ICI factory at Tuckingmill, on the edge of Camborne, a 14-acre site with 250,000 square feet of covered workshops.

The site had been originally developed by Bickford Smith & Co, inventor and manufacturers of the mining safety fuse. Now Teagle Machinery, having

sold most of the farm land, had the necessary capital to purchase it. The acquisition greatly increased the company's manufacturing capacity and very soon the first machines, including the Speediloader Automatic Pick-up elevator, the Junior and Senior trailer-spreaders and the AT1 hay tedder, were leaving the factory gate. Some research and development work was undertaken at Tuckingmill and the accounts and design aspects were transferred there from the Blackwater factory. This did not change until 1968 when a new, purpose-built office block was built at the Blackwater works.

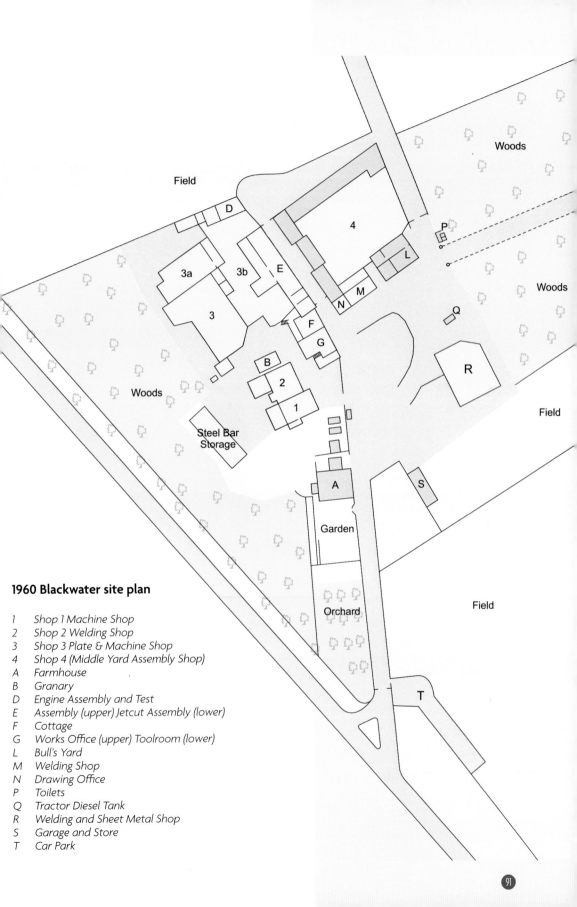

1960 Blackwater site plan

1 Shop 1 Machine Shop
2 Shop 2 Welding Shop
3 Shop 3 Plate & Machine Shop
4 Shop 4 (Middle Yard Assembly Shop)
A Farmhouse
B Granary
D Engine Assembly and Test
E Assembly (upper) Jetcut Assembly (lower)
F Cottage
G Works Office (upper) Toolroom (lower)
L Bull's Yard
M Welding Shop
N Drawing Office
P Toilets
Q Tractor Diesel Tank
R Welding and Sheet Metal Shop
S Garage and Store
T Car Park

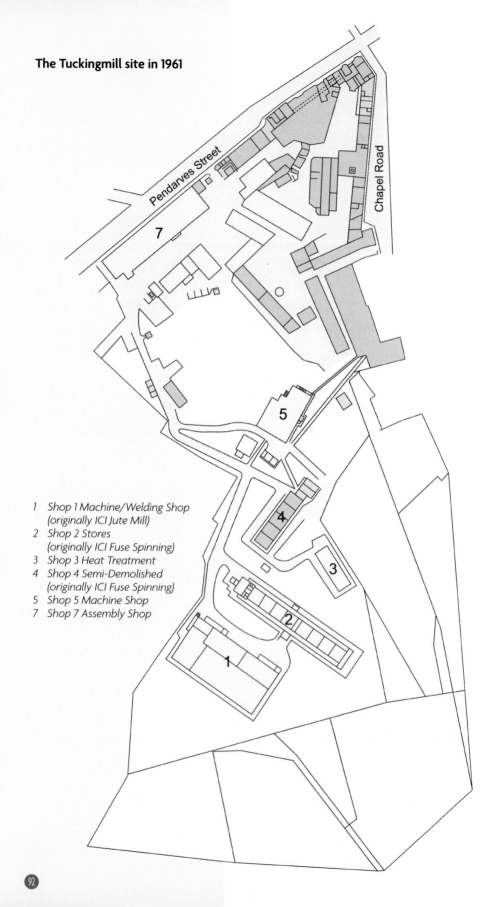

The Tuckingmill site in 1961

1 Shop 1 Machine/Welding Shop
  (originally ICI Jute Mill)
2 Shop 2 Stores
  (originally ICI Fuse Spinning)
3 Shop 3 Heat Treatment
4 Shop 4 Semi-Demolished
  (originally ICI Fuse Spinning)
5 Shop 5 Machine Shop
7 Shop 7 Assembly Shop

The Tuckingmill factory facade which fronts the main Redruth to Camborne road – Pendarves Street, largely unaltered since it was built in the mid-1800s

The Royal Smithfield Show was for manufacturers rather than agents and in 1960 the Teagle directors felt that it was time they had a presence there. There were many new machines on show including, on stand 217, eight which had been made by W T Teagle Machinery Ltd, a clear indication of the company's continued emphasis on invention and innovation. From that year, the event was a regular feature of the calendar. Fred recalled that in that first year their stand was in a remote corner of the second floor, next to the gents' toilet. It was so small that the machines had to be stacked in double-decker style.

Another year it was near a bar and, at the end of each day, they had to return all of the glass tankards which had been left by people visiting their stand. Fred said, "Not all were returned and from then on there was never a shortage of tankards in the Teagle households!" On one occasion, Tom was invited to take part in an interview with the Minister of Agriculture. At the time, the Labour Government was giving farmers a tough time and Tom refused to meet him, saying, "I want nothing to do with him or his party!"

Anthony Solway joined the company in 1961 and was there for 49 years, until he retired in 2010. At first, he was involved in cutting and drilling but most of his time there was spent working at a lathe. It was a job that he must have enjoyed as he later bought one for his own use at home. He now spends his time refurbishing his superb collection of motorbikes, some dating from the 1940s.

Sometime during the late 1980s, Anthony tired of piecework and when the opportunity arose he transferred to the experimental section – Tom Teagle's pride and joy. By then, however, Tom was in the very late stages of his life and their time working together was brief.

Anthony said, "I'd worked with him on other projects and he was always in and around the various workshops. I got on with him well but some thought him a bit hard. I reckon that there was always a reason for it. If someone did something that upset him they would discover that he had a long memory." However, as Mike Stephens pointed out, once it was sorted it was sorted!

Tom, walking through the experimental department, came across an operator making a component for one of his projects. "How's it coming on?" he asked. "'Tis pretty good Cap'n", was the reply. Taken aback, Tom exclaime: "Pretty good!? – Pretty good id'n good enough for me; 'tis got to be zackly! (exactly)". The operator checked the dimensions on the components. It was 'spot on'. "See 'ere Cap'n 'tiz zackly!" "Ah well", Tom said "If 'tis zackly, 'tis fine with me", and walked on.

During his 49 years with the company, Anthony saw considerable fluctuations in the workload, and in the workforce, but somehow there was always enough work to keep them going.

When the remainder of the farmland was sold, sometime around 1962, Tom Teagle collected together all of the implements that had been used on the farm and placed them on "the island." Mike Stephens spotted a chain harrow which he thought would be handy on his father's farm. He asked if he could buy it. Tom was happy to sell it to him and even lent him a tractor and trailer to transport it home. A few days later, however, Tom asked if he could buy it back. It transpired that it was never Tom's to sell. It belonged to Noel Hoskins of Greenacres Farm.

The Tedders

1962 – The AT1 tedder

The AT1 tedder with swathboard

The tedder or hay tedder is used to aerate or fluff up mown hay to speed up the drying process. Its use dates from around the 1850s when a two-wheeled horse-drawn machine with wire tines replaced the farm worker with his pitchfork.

The late 1950 versions were mostly horse-driven machines adapted for use by tractors. However, when Teagles entered the market it was with a fully mounted version, firstly single row but soon two and three-row machines.

The Dominant tedder followed in 1967. This was a rotary tedding machine designed for one, two and four rows. Following some early problems, solid steel tines replaced the spring versions which were prone to snap off. After that, the machine worked well. Perhaps surprisingly, its popularity did not spread beyond the South-West but this could have been more to do with the lack of a sales team than any problem with the design.

Manufacture ceased during the 1970s and David Teagle suggested that the machine was ten years ahead of its time. The market was simply not ready for it.

In 1974 *The Scottish Farming Leader* included a photograph and article about a new design of rotary tedder which had caught its reporter's eye at the Royal Smithfield Show – the Teagle AB hay maker. He referred to it as a mounted machine of ingenious design which differed from the rest in that both rotors rotated in the same direction, a fact which offered many advantages.

The 1995 high-speed Superted 160 and the 220 Swath Conditioner were designed to aerate silage, hay or straw to aid the drying process and reduce the nutrient loss

1968 – The four-row Dominant tedder

The
Mowers and Toppers

Heavier crops and the increasing size of tractors led manufacturers to design rotary mowers to cut silage and hay. Most of those on the market, however, were rear-mounted which meant that the tractor wheels flattened the crop before the mower could cut it.

To overcome this, the Teagle designers, with their dislike of complicated linkages and gearboxes, designed a belt-driven totally offset, six foot cut, rotary mower that would fold for transport. It proved to be too wide for most farmers but the design was established and soon, five foot Matchless mowers were leaving the factory. By the late summer of 1967 a good number were operating in Cornish fields.

The machine must surely be rated as one of the success stories because in that year, after a one-day demonstration in Victoria, Australia, an order for 240 machines arrived.

The 1969 Matchless Mk 3 rotary mower

1969 – Another load of Matchless mowers heading for the A30

It proved to be virtually indestructible and many reports were received that the Matchless had destroyed other pieces of machines lost in the grass but in each case there was no damage to the mower.

In 1967, following several enquiries from customers on the continent, Fred and Dinah Teagle took a Matchless mower, for demonstrations in Holland, Germany, Switzerland and Austria. Customs in Belgium made life difficult for them by insisting they needed a carnet for the trailer, but after several hours of discussion and delay accepted the trailer was a part of the mower and strapped them together with customs seals. The Dutch were enthusiastic about the mower, the Austrians felt it important that the machine could be seen working on the side of a mountain, the Germans kept muttering about it being an 'Ausländermaschine' (foreign machine) and the Swiss, because grass was so valuable to them, 'were only able to let us loose in a half acre of orchard' – not the best site to demonstrate a high-speed mower. Despite the difficult conditions encountered on the trip, some machines were sold following the demonstrations.

1967, Fred and Dinah about to set out with a Matchless mower on a demonstration tour of Holland, Germany, Switzerland and Austria

Mower Success of Cornish Firm

A Cornish firm which claims its mower is the fastest yet made has just sold 240 machines to Australian farmers. W T Teagle (Machinery) Ltd of Blackwater, Truro, put their rotary mower on show at Wangaratta, Australia, recently and 135 were sold in one day.

A spokesman for the firm said that the sales augured well for the future as Australian farmers could make their choice from all countries. The farmer demands that his machinery is tough and free from servicing trouble as often his farm is half a day's journey from a repair depot. The mower was developed last year and is tractor operated. It has fewer working parts than any other mower.

Preparing for the demonstration in Holland

1969 – The Matchless mower on display at a show in Melbourne, Australia. The machine was sent over and displayed by Australian agent John Byron Ltd Pasture Toppers.

1977 – The Mk 1 Topper 8

The Topper range was introduced in 1977. It proved to be an effective and popular product for removing the long dead grass and weed, leaving three to four inches of fresh grass with a chance to flourish.

1979 – Bedford YCV 795T with a load of Mk l Topper 8s

The Mk 2 Topper 8 (eight-foot wide) was introduced in 1984. It replaced the earlier model and was fabricated as a monocoque design in which the strength comes from the external skin, similar to an eggshell. It was easier to manufacture than the previous models and its ease of use proved an attractive benefit to the farmer.

1995 saw the arrival of the Topper 510 with its six-foot wide cut. It was well built, very affordable and well received. For some, though, it was too wide and before long a four-foot and five-foot model joined the range.

A further development was the Topper 8 Offset – a fully offset machine. This had the great advantage of being set to one side so that the grass was not flattened by the tractor wheels. Any difficulty in transporting it to and from the field was overcome by the machine being hydraulically swivelled to a position directly behind the tractor.

A load of Mk 2 Topper 8s ready for despatch in spring 1986

1984 – The Mk 2 Topper 8

1995 – The Topper 510

There was a silver lining for the company during the 2001 foot-and-mouth disaster – with grass growing and no livestock to eat it, the demand for pasture toppers took off.

1999 – The Topper 8 Offset pasture topper had the great advantage of leaving no wheel marks and could be swivelled hydraulically for easier transportation

To increase the company's impact on the grass-topping market the Berti flail-mower was imported in 2002 – a decision which made a huge penetration into the market

The Berti front-mounted flail-mower working at the Eden Project

2003 – The Topper 9 available for front or rear mounting is the widest machine that can travel on the road in the working position

2004 – The range of Dynamo finishing mowers extended the product range into the amenity market and machines began to be used on playing fields, golf courses and parks

2007 – The EF 120 engine-drive flail-mower further extended the range – a heavy-duty product that could be pulled by quad bikes to clear rough grass and small bushes where conditions were too difficult for finishing mowers

The
Trailers

It could be said that the entire business began with a trailer as the very first product was a tipping cart. Of course, that was back in 1937, and any comparison with the huge machines that leave the factory gate in 2015 will show how far the company has travelled in its journey to become one of the leading agricultural machine manufacturers.

During the 1960s, most silage was being carried in small-capacity trailers and the prospect of a much larger version caused quite a stir. The Titan 7 filled a long-awaited need. It sold in large quantities and totally changed the market's idea of Teagles as a producer of light-duty machinery. Soon, there were about 4,000 Titan trailers working in the South-West and before long there was also a spreader version and a dump trailer available.

The 1969 all-steel prototype Titan 7 twin-axle tipping trailer being used by David Lugg, Fred's brother-in-law, to move sand from a beach

The Titan 7 silage trailer

In 1972 the trailer range was extended to include the Tiger 45 (4.5-ton), the Tiger 60 (6-ton) and the Titan (7, 8 and the 10-ton shown here)

1974 – The Titan 7 and 10-ton dump trailer – its solid construction made it ideal for heavy earth moving on industrial sites

1980 – The Tiger 45 trailer

1980 – The Tiger 60 trailer

1983 – Pair of Toucans working in West Cornwall

1983 – Splitting the forage harvester from the trailer

The
Forage Wagons

During the 1970s large numbers of loader wagons were being imported from the continent for use on British farms. The challenge for the design team was not simply to compete with the continentals but to produce a sturdier machine and one which had an efficient chopping mechanism.

The prototype used an old and heavily modified Tarrup harvester fitted to a Triumph 6-ton trailer but the real problem lay in finding a suitable chopping machine that was short enough and compatible with the trailer. The JF 110 forage harvester was the only one which ticked all the boxes and so began an association with the JF Company which saw the combination of a Teagle forage wagon and a JF harvester.

Prototype forage wagon with the Tarrup single-chop forage harvester

1980 – The prototype Toucan 6 precision-chop forage wagon with a JF Harvester

1980 – The Toucan 7

1982 – The Toucan 8

THE ROYAL HIGHLAND SHOW

1983

SILVER MEDAL

FOR

NEW IMPLEMENT

Sponsored By

National Westminster Bank

Awarded to *Teagle Machinery Ltd.*

for *Teagle Toucan Forage Wagon*

Secretary
The Royal Highland and Agricultural Society of Scotland

Another award – this time at the 1983 Royal Highland Show

The family were clearly delighted at the four awards in one year for the Toucan as shown in the spring issue of the 1984 Toucan News

Toucan news

Published by: Teagle Machinery Limited, Blackwater, Truro, Cornwall TR4 8HQ.
Telephone: Truro (0872) 560592, Telex: 45573   Issue: **Spring 1984**

Teagle

Country-wide Success

4 Awards in one year for the Toucan

SILVER MEDAL
(1983)

above:
HRH Prince of Wales presenting Silver Medal award at Dairy Farming Event 1983

NEW EQUIPMENT AWARDS
BARCLAYS

ROYAL HIGHLAND SHOW 1983
NEW IMPLEMENT AWARD

below:
Silver Medal presentation at Royal Highland Show 1983

above: Fred and John Teagle receiving 1983 Royal Show Silver Medal from His Excellency Sir Shridath Ramphal, Commonwealth Secretary General.

left: Silver Medal awarded by Royal Welsh Agricultural Society, 1983

In contrast to the imported loader wagons, the Toucan forage wagon was a precision-chop machine. It was sturdy, well constructed and had the great advantage that it could be converted to a conventional tipping trailer at the end of the silage season.

The harvester unit was mounted on a sub-chassis which could be removed in a matter of minutes. Its wheels followed the contours of the ground with about three-quarters of its weight transferred onto the tractor drawbar. This, together with an effective hydraulic braking system, enabled it to be used on slopes that were unsuitable for conventional harvester units.

No matter what line of business you are in, it is always satisfying to come away from an event with an award. The Royal Highland Show in 1983 proved a happy hunting ground as Teagles collected the silver medal in the new implement section with their Toucan Forage Wagon.

The Teagle trailer and the JF harvester had been a very successful combination but in the late 1980s it became clear that the supply of the JF 110 was to cease. The continued supply of this important combination was in jeopardy but, as with so many other products, the design team quickly produced a replacement and over the next four or five years Teagles produced their own precision-chop harvester.

The Siler

Following some interesting experimental work on straw shredders in the mid 1980s, the company made a unique forage harvester called the Siler. This machine had a direct drive to its cutting rotor, doing away with the expensive gearboxes and drivelines. The rotor was equipped with approximately 120 cutting blades, worked against the same number of stationary blades giving a simple, easily maintained system of chopping the silage. The edge of the rotor was equipped with 16 impeller blades to blow the crop evenly into the trailer.

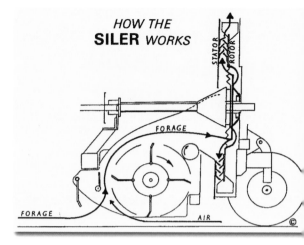

1985 – Siler Forage Harvester

The Trailer-Spreaders and Spreaders

1963 – The Spread-a-Box was a novel innovation for the smaller farmer to enable him to use his indispensable tractor box as a dung spreader

1963 – Trailer / Spreaders

The "**TEAGLE** SENIOR"
FOUR - TON *Trailer Spreader*

1968 – The 275, 360 and 720 side spreaders

Continuing with the theme of multi-functional machines, the idea of a range of dung spreaders that could also be used as trailers had to be a winner. In 1963, a small range of 2.5 and 4-ton versions were designed.

They were originally made with moving floors, spreading rotors and wooden bodies. They did the job well but the industry was moving forward at a pace and they proved to be just a stepping-stone to the next generation – an all-steel version made possible by the installation of the press-brake machines in the factory. The complexity of the drive to the rotors had held back development but now, with that problem overcome, the design team could begin work on a larger model which would double the capacity.

The side spreaders were intended to compete with other versions on the market but a unique selling point was needed and this was found with the incorporation of a dozer blade in the drum to force the load onto the rotor. This made the machine much more efficient in providing an even-density spread throughout the load. Another feature was that it could feed clamp silage to cattle.

The 7-ton Titan trailer-spreader arrived in 1970. It was a heavy-duty machine, one of the largest machines available in the country at that time. It had high-capacity spreader rotors providing a high output and accurate spread-pattern albeit with low horsepower. It was a tremendous step forward for both the company and the industry in general.

When the Cornish firm of Crompton and Warden ceased trading, Teagles considered their dung/slurry spreader design worth taking over. A batch was produced with the name Trojan but, for some reason, the industry did not take to this dual-purpose machine. After just one batch it was discontinued in favour of the standard form of side spreader.

The Tornado side spreader was originally produced with a capacity of either 5.5 or 7 cubic yards with the body supported by a separate chassis. It was later modified to have a neater and stronger monocoque construction. The bearings that supported the rotor were positioned away from the slurry and the front chain guard was constructed as a substantial support to the front plate.

There was still a demand for a rear discharge spreader but rather than begin producing a new line it was decided to import the Le Boulch version from France. Following some further development and modifications it proved to be a successful addition to the range and many were sold. However, difficulties arose within the Le Boulch company and it seemed that Teagles would, once again, be faced with the prospect

The 7-ton Titan trailer-spreader

This November 1973 photograph is from an advertisement for R J Hewitt (Farms) Ltd, Agricultural Contractors of Godalming in Surrey. Its claim was that 400 cubic yards of dung were spread in a day using the Titan spreaders and 10-ton trailers.

1983 – Trojan dual spreader

The 1985 Tornado 700 side-spreader

2001 – The Le Boulch spreader

of not being able to offer a rear discharge spreader. So, after a break of over 30 years, the company decided to produce its own version. The Titan 10 and Titan 12 rear-discharge spreaders were more robust, easier to maintain and provided a much better spreading mechanism. It was a big step forward but success often brings problems and now it was one of production capacity. With confidence in the product, further investment was made and the range developed to include smaller models of six, eight and nine cubic metres and larger models of 15 to 18 cubic metres.

2011 – The Titan 10 and Titan 12 rear-discharge spreaders

The
Crop-Drying Fans

1965 – The Thermoblast crop drying fans

Tom Teagle's inventive mind next turned to crop-drying. He thought that if damp baled hay was stacked it would generate its own heat which could then be used to dry the rick without the use of an exterior heat source.

After several years of experimenting, a high-pressure fan was developed to force cold air through ricks of stacked bales for short periods to circulate the naturally occurring heat. By careful monitoring it was possible to produce barn dried hay at a fraction of the cost of more conventional methods. It was a completely new way of tackling the problem and the marketing department had the difficult task of convincing the customer that it would work. The Ministry of Agriculture's advisors were similarly sceptical but the idea gradually caught on and the satisfied customers soon became a team of unpaid salesmen.

A touch of humour always helps and this front page of a 1978 brochure does just that

A consignment of crop-drying fans awaiting departure in 1966

Alan Combellack began working at Tuckingmill in January 1964 – in Shop 1. Gerald Triggs was the foreman at that time. At first Alan was involved in cutting and drilling but then he was given the chance to do some welding. He grabbed the opportunity and for the next 18 years, until he left when Tuckingmill closed, he was one of the welding team. He said, "I decided not to move to Blackwater but that didn't mean that I wasn't happy working for the company. There was a good level of camaraderie and during the lunch breaks we either enjoyed playing football in the yard or a game of euchre while we ate our lunch."

Alan Dell joined the company just a month later and was also based at Tuckingmill. At that time, most of the spray-painting was done outside and components were moved from shop to shop by a tractor pulling a convoy of small trailers. He said, "Compared to today it all sounds a bit archaic but at that time it was how it was done. We were a forward-looking company making their own machines and even working for the Ministry of Defence and for Holmans. When I started, there were about 45 men working there but the number quickly grew to about 60. After about ten years I was made foreman of

the fabrication shop and when Tuckingmill closed, in 1984, I transferred to Blackwater until I retired in 2006."

Ken Beard lived in Goonown and was a familiar and popular character around the Blackwater factory with his large physique and beard to match. Mike Stephens described him as a powerful chap who would take more than his fair share of the load. One day they had to take the gas cutting gear to the other side of the yard so Ken gave Mike the torch to carry while he took the two large gas bottles – one under each arm.

Over the years, the company has had many foremen and managers including Les Roberts and Bob Fowler, who shared the role during the early years. Les lived at Tywarnhayle Lodge, a pair of cottages formerly owned by the company, situated next to a little wood at the end of the drive that led to Silverwell. The position was then taken up by Frank Caldicott who managed both factories until he relinquished his place at Blackwater to concentrate his efforts at Tuckingmill. Brian Swallow took over at the Blackwater factory and, when Frank left the company, Bob Fowler returned as works manager at Tuckingmill. Brian was the works manager at Blackwater for many years and when he retired John Veall took over.

Clive Mitchell began working in the Tuckingmill cut-off shop in 1965. The wide variety of work suited him and he quickly gained experience of welding, paint-spraying and even lathe work. In the early days, all the steel had to be unloaded by hand – barred off and put in outside racks, as Tom Moses described it. Alan Combellack talked of George Hocking, a short but powerfully built man. He said, "Some of the stuff was pretty heavy and there were four of us lifting it – three at one end and George at the other".

Every company seems to have its share of industrial problems and in June 1965 work virtually ceased at Blackwater when most of the staff downed tools. The problem related to pay and, before long, 87 men had gathered outside the factory to discuss their grievances. The news travelled fast and within hours about a third of the Tuckingmill workforce walked out in support. (With temperatures rising fast at the factory Fred was well away from the scene – he had recently married Dinah Lugg and they were on their honeymoon.)

The dispute arose out of a claim that there was a lack of proper organisation leading to a reduced continuity of work. This, the men contended, was affecting piece-work earnings. Claims and counterclaims were exchanged as the shop stewards accused Tom Teagle of refusing to negotiate. Tom responded that the accusation was "absolutely and completely inaccurate". He also dismissed suggestions of a lack of continuity of work saying, "We have more work than we can do". As to the claim of a reduced level of piece-work, he pointed out that the time spent on it was currently well above the previous year.

With feelings running high, the AEU shop stewards asked their National Executive to declare the strike official. Later, however, the shop stewards denied that they were actually on strike, claiming that they had simply refused to work on one day as a protest and would have returned if the management had allowed them in.

Tom Moses, one of the drivers, recalled returning from an "upcountry" run and being told by Mrs Teagle that the men were on strike. He knew nothing of the problem and was reluctant to join in but she said that perhaps it would be best for him if he did. Tom said, "It was a Friday and the men were meeting up at the stone depot, by the crossroads, so I went up to join them. Before long, Tom Teagle came up and said that he would like to have a few words. He talked for a while and then told us that he didn't need us as much as we needed him. It was all very amicable but then he said that after they had finished their meeting he wanted them all to come down the drive in an orderly manner where they could collect their cards. He'd fired every one of us." Tom Moses collected his and went home but when he looked in

1964 – The Teagle float in the St Agnes Carnival which shows its lines of supply to many countries across the world – despite the clear message, many St Agnes people remained unaware that they had a world-class company on their doorstep

the envelope he found a note which said that if anyone wished to be reinstated, they should apply on Saturday morning when the company would consider taking them back. Tom jumped in his car and went straight back and when Mrs Teagle asked him what he wanted he showed her the note. Just then, Tom Teagle walked up the passage and asked, "And what did the note say?" Tom Moses said that it replied that if he wished to be reinstated he should apply on Saturday morning. "Well," said Mr Teagle, "what are you doing here now?" "I told him that I was getting married the next day. He didn't say anything: he fetched a new contract of employment and handed it to me. I looked at it and asked how I should answer the first question. It asked whether I was married or single. He took it back from me, tore it up and gave me twenty pounds. I had my job back and a wedding present."

Those who wanted to be re-engaged had to agree to fresh terms as they were considered to have discharged themselves by walking out. Tensions were high but the first sign of a resolution came when 17 men applied to resume work. They were re-engaged. The union announced that it deplored the decision to dismiss its members, but hoped that it would be possible for all the men to return to work under their old contracts. There was talk of a stalemate, and of a full-time AEU official being sent to Cornwall to help with negotiations, but within a few days half the workforce was back at work. Shortly after, the remainder asked for their jobs back. The stoppage suited no one and Tom Teagle agreed that all but four could return. Three of them were the shop stewards.

Brian Hutchins recalled the event, which took place just a few years after he began working there. He said, "Even we boys joined in but we didn't really understand the implications, we were just swept along on the tide. Looking back now I feel that

it could have been avoided with a bit more discussion. Tom Teagle was prone to hire and fire on a whim, something that wouldn't happen so readily these days, but there was another side to him. Later, in the mid-1970s, we were on short time, sometimes just two or three days a week. It was hard for those who had a family to support and did generate some ill-feeling but we were kept on when there wasn't really enough work. I'm sure that cost the company a lot of money."

Mike Stephens was at home when he heard that Tom Teagle was re-engaging the strikers. He discussed it with Dick Littlejohns and they eventually decided to ask for their jobs back. He said, "Tom Teagle was standing in the yard as we walked down and after saying good morning we asked if we could come back to work. He told us to go up to the office to see Brian Swallow. We knew then that we were all right."

Tom Moses recalled an occasion when he lost his wallet while on a trip to Anglesey. He said that it took just one phone call to Mrs Teagle and it was all sorted. She arranged accommodation and enough money until he returned home. He said, "I offered to repay it a number of times but Mr Teagle kept stalling. Eventually he told me to forget it. The family treated me well and when my wife was in hospital with cancer Mrs Teagle visited her every day and even bought her cotton nightdresses because she reckoned the nylon ones were too hot for her."

A little later there was a walk-out of a very different kind when someone claimed that there was a bomb in the factory. It must have been with some urgency that everyone poured out through the doors and gathered in the yard. No one was ever sure whether it was a hoax or a misunderstanding but it turned out to be a false alarm and they returned to work.

On one occasion the local hunt came to call and chased an unfortunate fox down the drive and around the loading area. Eventually, it took cover in Tom Teagle's garage, behind where the main office now stands. The pursuing dogs had its scent and it was soon cornered. Fox hunting is guaranteed to raise passions one way or the other and the commotion from the yard soon brought the workforce out. They did their best to drive off the hounds but the animals were not to be denied. Anthony Solway recalled the horrific screams as the fox was torn apart.

He said, "The sight of the creature being held aloft sickened us".

The company booklet *Two Dozen Ways of Increasing Your Profits* was a clever way to promote the products. It drew people in who were hoping to find the answer and how better to discover it than by reading about the wide range of products on offer? It also included the story that in 1948 it had taken two years to sell seven broadcasters but, since then, production of that particular machine had sometimes exceeded one thousand a month.

Transport

The lorries in the early fleet were an essential feature of the distribution network but they were far removed from the giants of today with their sophisticated electronics and sleeper cabs. Like the cars of yesteryear, they were maintained by mechanics with spanners and wrenches rather than the diagnostic tools now required to keep vehicles running smoothly. The laws have also changed over the years and it is quite amazing to think of deliveries being made across the country with vehicles restricted to 20 mph.

Tom Moses was living at St Newlyn East when he began working at Teagles as a driver – that was in 1963 or 1964. He said, "I officially retired in 2002 or thereabouts but I kept my licence and am still putting in a full working week. Apart from that, I keep myself busy making remote-controlled model boats, some even powered by steam. My first lorry was a Thames Trader with a box canopy over the cab where we could carry five concrete mixers or whatever."

The additional payload provided by the canopy was an important financial benefit – sufficient to cover the cost of the vehicle's road fund licence.

When Tom Moses began working for the company he covered the UK, delivering

1950 – An early Teagle Guy Otter Diesel with driver Tom James

machines to all the small agents. It meant finding his way around the narrow roads as he moved from village to village. Considering the size of the fleet, the logistical problem of delivering the right machine to the right agent was enormous. "But," said Tom, "Mary Teagle had it sorted. Each driver had 40 or 50 deliveries to make and maybe some steel collections as well. Mrs Teagle would give us a batch of typewritten notes arranged in village order. She must have had a brain like a computer. If you dropped a machine at the wrong place you could hear her voice as you

This 1950s LWB Hillmaster, manufactured at Dobwalls, near Liskeard, was included in Peter Tutthill's book "The Cornish Commercial Vehicle"

drove home, you knew what you were going to get!" This complex system of delivery changed over time as it became the usual practice to centralise drops to main agents rather than using the many sub-agents.

Helping Mary Teagle was Mrs Luke of St Agnes who undertook the secretarial work, took the orders, processed the invoices and carried out the many tasks which helped the company tick. It was clearly a busy office and for these two ladies, the days must have been hectic. Prior to Mrs Luke working there it was Miss Pearce from Peterville who helped in the office.

Selwood Magor made most of the overseas deliveries but, as sales increased, it became necessary to send more than one lorry and Tom Moses regularly found himself on the French run. It involved a crossing from Southampton to Le Havre and, although most trips went smoothly, there was one in particular that stuck in his mind. It involved a gendarme and by the sound of it he was the original bold gendarme. A problem with the gearbox meant that Tom could not change gear and when he came to a road junction he had to decide whether to stop or drive on. He could see that the road was clear but unfortunately he did not see the gendarme concealed in the bushes. Suddenly, there he was, and Tom had no choice but to put the brakes on. The gendarme strode over and said, "In England stop means stop and it's the same in France, what is your excuse?"

Tom explained that he had a mechanical problem and could not change gear. This seemed to fall on sympathetic ears but as the voice of the law mellowed he asked Tom if he had any cigarettes. Tom knew that he was in a difficult situation so he gave him and his fellow officer a packet of free-issues which drivers received on the boat. It was clear that this was not quite enough as it was followed by, "And

Circa 1965 – The Thames Trader with the canopy

cigarettes for my wife". Following that, he was left to wrestle with the gearbox and drive away without a fine. That was not the end of it, however, as every time Tom drove that way he was stopped by the same gendarme with the same request: "Cigarettes for my wife".

On another trip, one of the injectors on Tom's lorry failed. He said, "Selwood Magor was with me on that occasion, we were travelling in convoy. It was just as well as he was a good mechanic. Even so, he had a problem. The old injector was a bit reluctant to come out until, that is, he used an old mechanic's trick. He removed all the bolts and started the engine. It came out like a rocket. He soon had the new one in place and we were on our way again." Fred Teagle recalled that both men used to return with conkers for his sons. Apparently horse chestnuts grow very large over there.

Another consignment across the water was a small load of machinery bound for the Isles of Scilly. Tom drove down to meet the Scillonian at Penzance but discovered that they would only accept deliveries by rail. That was the policy and that was what they would stick to. It all seemed a bit strange but he had to drive the few miles back to St Erth where he loaded the items onto the train. They then travelled by rail

The 1966 fleet

to Penzance and were dropped off just a few yards from where he had parked in the first place.

All of the loading and unloading at the Blackwater factory took place outside, and if it was raining then you donned a raincoat. Tom said, "I had to reverse to the loading area, "the island" as it was called, and rain or shine I just carried on". The open area in the centre of the Blackwater factory complex has always been referred to as "the island". It still exists but, whereas it had once been rough ground, in 1955 it was made more useable by being tidied

up and enclosed by retaining walls. Five years later the entire area was levelled and concreted and it is now a large space for storage with lorry loading ramps and an open-air work area.

By 1965 almost all deliveries in the UK were made using road transport, vehicles owned by the company or by outside contractors. The famous Thames Traders were in use then but as it became necessary to carry larger loads the Ford D series replaced them. At that time these were big lorries – over 30 feet long and more economical for the longer trips.

Bedford YCV 795T with a load of Dynacut hedge-trimmers bound for France

A mixed load in 1996

September 2001 and another load of Tomahawk 9090s leaves the factory

2005 – A trio of Scanias

2006 – Bound for Ireland

Alongside a photograph of a lorry on its way to France with a load of hedge-trimmers, the *Sunday Independent* included an article with the caption, "Lorry Tax protest". It reported that the Road Haulage Association had clashed with the Government over its proposal to further increase road tax. If implemented, it would follow an increase of one third in vehicle excise duty in the 1975 budget and 7.5 pence on the price of a gallon of diesel in April 1976. The RHA said that it would mean companies would be forced to increase their prices. The lorry in the photograph was described as the biggest Bedford lorry in Cornwall and, as the intention was to link the amount of tax to the lorry size, the delivered cost of such machines would inevitably rise. Any such increase to the agents and farmers would ultimately mean an increase in the cost of food.

2008 – Destination Germany

1967 – Shop 1 at Blackwater during construction

The late 1960s were a period of intense development activity. At times, it seemed that the Blackwater factory was a permanent building site. In 1965, to the right of the access road, Fred and Dinah Teagle's house was being built and a few years later, in 1972, they acquired some new neighbours when his brother, David and his wife, Glynis, moved into their new home, Bryannack.

A rather larger development was also under way in 1965. An aircraft hangar which had been in use at St Eval Aerodrome was being erected and was to be the new Shop 5, to be used for collection, marshalling and distribution of products or, as some described it, a big loading bay. It covered about half an acre but even that did not prove to be large enough as it was doubled in area in 1971.

An enclosed overhead conveyor was removed from the old ICI factory at Tuckingmill in 1966 and taken to Blackwater where it was installed to run between Shops 2 and 4. Located between Shops 1 and 3, Shop 2 was

where the components were primed. The items were slung on hooks beneath the conveyor, transported through the dip-tank and then at high level to Shop 4 where they were assembled and painted. The conveyor housing passed over the generator house, so what better use for that spare hot air than to help with the drying process? Rather than let it go to waste it was ducted up to the overhead conveyor and, by the time that the parts had reached their destination, the primer was dry.

This conveyor served its purpose for 36 years but in 2002 it had to go. Components had now become too large to travel through the housing and, apart from that, it posed a height problem for vehicles passing below. Following a few collisions it was decided to begin its demolition.

A further element of the improvements programme was put in place in 1967 when Shop 1 was demolished and replaced by another hangar from St Eval. It was where much of the sheet and plate metalwork was carried out.

The construction of a new, purpose-built office block in 1968 at Blackwater brought great changes. It was sufficiently large to incorporate many of the head-office functions under one roof and within a very short time the design and accounts departments were transferred there from Tuckingmill. Quite apart from any efficiency benefits, this must have been a big step forward in the creation of a "major-company" image.

David Teagle joined the "family firm" in 1967. This followed a short period with accountants Balme, Kitchen and Pearce but despite this initial involvement in the financial world, his first activities were in advertising, organising the parts department and selling the products.

In 1973, however, normal service was resumed when he returned to the world of the calculator. Brian May, the company accountant, had left and the double-entry ledgers and balance sheets landed firmly in David's lap. He found himself on a very steep learning curve but he grasped the opportunity and was soon occupying the finance director's chair. David said, "We had a wages clerk but my first challenge was the ledgers which were all done by hand. We soon had a software package in place and while that presented me with

a new challenge, it did make the job a lot less laborious." In 2010, David's son, Robin joined the company and before long he was looking after the sales ledger and wages. Robin had a somewhat strange route into the finance team, having been a professional football player with Plymouth Argyle, a worker at the Eden Project and a trainee with an electrical company. Indeed, he originally joined the company as an electrical apprentice before transferring to the accounts department.

Gary Richards began working at Tuckingmill on the 12th August 1968. It was about three weeks after he had left school that he and his father were driving past the main gate when they decided to call in to enquire whether there was any chance of a job. It was as well that they did, as he was immediately offered employment. He spent just three weeks in the factory before beginning a 12-month, full-time course at Cornwall Technical College. On completion of his time at the "Tech" he began work in earnest, in the cut-off shop, where he became acquainted with the machines used to cut, drill and guillotine the steel. From there, he moved to the experimental shop and this gave him the opportunity to develop his skills on the lathes, a prelude to a long career in precision engineering. Later, after a move from Tuckingmill to Blackwater, he was placed in charge of Shop 7 where the precision machining was carried out.

During the early days of life at Tuckingmill, all the material and components were moved by muscle power. Huge steel plates, sometimes three-quarter-inch thick, were unloaded and moved by hand, but when the Shop 1 extension was complete the new overhead cranes made life considerably easier.

In 1969 it was Tuckingmill's turn for expansion. A new Shop 1, measuring 200 feet by 60 feet, was erected and would be used for fabrication and welding. Its completion brought the total covered area there to 150,000 square feet. Even this was insufficient, however, and two additional bays were added four years later.

The talk in December 1969 was of the credit squeeze and at the Royal Smithfield Show there were many downcast faces on the stands. On the Teagle stand, however, it was a rather different story. There, the Universal Tipmix, a tractor-mounted concrete mixer, was proving to be a winner. A large order from France for 50 machines a month for the next 12 months had made the trip worthwhile.

Agricultural shows were now an important feature, with a first visit to Amsterdam and a return to Paris – for the sixth year in a row. Fred Teagle and his two brothers, David and John, were there to describe the benefits of the range but there were other, more distant, shows where importers played that role – in Verona, Vienna, Zaragoza, Australia, Toronto and elsewhere.

1969 – The new fabrication shop being erected at Tuckingmill

1969 – David Teagle at a trade show in Verona, Northern Italy

The 1970s

The new 1970 logo

In 1970 it was time for a change in corporate image. The old name of W T Teagle (Machinery) Ltd had stood the test of time but after almost 30 years it was to be simplified. In future it would be Teagle Machinery Ltd.

The 1970 Canada Farm and Industrial Equipment Show in Toronto provided an interesting and rather amusing story involving Tom Teagle. He had finished erecting his display and wandered over to the Ransomes, Sims and Jefferies stand for a chat. They seemed to be struggling a bit so he offered to help them set up some of their machines. His offer was gratefully accepted and he began assembling a plough. It could be that his motivation was a bit of industrial espionage but at the end of the show he was back there again, helping to dismantle it.

Russell Fowler collected the pools money each week and many recall him wandering through the workshops shouting, "Football 'morra, let's have your money". Ron Hendry said that when you were on piece work you did not stop for anything. Once again, his story featured Russell Fowler who was busy welding when his spool of welding wire fell to the floor. Ron said, "He must have heard it drop but he continued welding as the reel rolled out of his cubicle and made its way down the factory. The floor had a slight fall on it and it didn't stop until it reached the end wall". Ron's memory of the piece work system was that it worked well but occasionally the target was almost impossible. Probably, he suggested, because someone had cheated the system and the rate had been adjusted.

Back in the 1970s Franklin Engelmann's BBC radio programme "Down your way" was a cult but it must have increased the local interest when it featured the familiar voice of Tom Teagle. The *Farm Engineering Industry* magazine of October 1970 referred to the broadcast and went on to outline the outstanding progress made by Teagle Machinery Ltd. It talked of broadcaster sales of 2,000 a month and an order from France for 4,000 such machines. Few people in neighbouring St Agnes would have realised the extent to which the company had grown and even now, in 2015, such figures will still be met with surprise. The report went on to say that they had 80% of the French hedge-trimmer market and were as well known in Australia as they were in Devon. Tom's choice of music was *The Blue Danube* to remind him, so the report suggested, "of the smooth, rhythmic fashion in which the export orders float in nowadays".

1970 – SIMA, Paris

Field

Woods

Woods

D

3a   3b   E

4

P

L

3

H
J
G

5

6

2

1

P

A

Q

Garden

Orchard

F

T

1970 Site Plan

1	Shop 1 Machine Shop
2	Shop 2 Welding Shop
3	Shop 3 Machine Shop
4	Shop 4 (Middle Yard Assembly Shop)
5	Shop 5 Loading Bay
6	Shop 6 Sheet Metal Shop
A	Farmhouse
D	Engine Assembly and Test
E	Tool Stores (upper) Jetcut Assembly (lower)
G	Works Office (upper) Toolroom (lower)
H	Overhead Conveyor
J	Generator
L	Paint Shop
P	Toilets
Q	Main Office
T	Car Park

This 1970 ticket for the dinner and dance suggests that the first one was held in 1969, a time when such events were more popular than they are today. Colin Vaughn provided the music and the tickets cost 32/- (£1.60). One year later and the third dinner and dance was held at the same venue with the same band but by December 1971 the country had "gone decimal" and the price of a ticket was £1.75.

These events continued for a number of years and one of those responsible for selling tickets was the mischievous Russell Fowler. Robbie Field was helping him and recalled going to St Agnes with him to bank the money. He said, "Russell was standing in the queue, wearing a balaclava which he suddenly pulled down over his face making him look like a bank robber. There were a few strange looks but I reckon that the staff must have known him because they made nothing of it."

August 1970 – Always keen to be involved in the social side of St Agnes life, the company entered a couple of vehicles in the carnival and David and John Teagle can be seen here exhibiting the old and the new

---

TEAGLE MACHINERY LTD.

SECOND ANNUAL

DINNER and DANCE

at the FALMOUTH HOTEL
on SATURDAY, 19th DECEMBER, 1970

Dancing to THE COLIN VAUGHN QUARTET

7.00 p.m. for 7.30 p.m.   Admission **32/-**

1971 – The loading bay extension in Shop 5 at Blackwater

1971 – A nostalgic view of the old farm stables and first floor barn which became the toolroom and works office above. To the right was the high-level conveyor between Shops 2 and 4 – directly above the generator house with its Rolls-Royce engine from which warm air was ducted to the conveyor to help dry the primed components as they made their way to the next stage of the process

With the introduction of mechanical horsepower the great shire horses were no longer needed and their departure meant that their home could be put to a new use. The ground floor became a toolroom and the first floor the production and drawing office – all pencil and paper in those days. Attractive as this building appears in the photograph, it was no longer fit for purpose and, in 1972, it was swept away and replaced by a new building for the works office and print room.

In line with its policy of keeping as much work as possible in-house, the company did most of its own printing, particularly the simple leaflets and price lists. At first, the material was produced on a Gestetner duplicating machine but later, a small offset litho printer was installed. This meant a marked improvement in quality. Initially, the print room was in the farmhouse but when the main office block was

built it moved to there. Another move followed in 1972 when the equipment was transferred to the new print room below the works office. Fred Teagle had always been involved in the design and printing of publications but, as demand grew, he became increasingly concerned that he was being sidetracked from his core function of machinery production. Something needed to change and, in 1974, to create some daylight between his two roles, he and Dinah created TeaglePrint, a separate company which would carry out work both for Teagle Machinery and for outside customers. They purchased all of the printing equipment,

The 1972 works office and print room below (photo taken sometime after removal of the conveyor)

1972 – Steelwork being erected for the new Blackwater Shop 3 – a machine shop

employed a graphic designer and invested in a larger printer, typesetting and darkroom equipment. Their resources also included a silkscreen printer on which they produced the decals for the machinery. During the printing company's 31 years it undertook a considerable amount of work but in 2005, with retirement looming, the partners decided to close the doors for the last time.

The experimental section, Shop 7, was built in 1971 and it was here that the new ideas were developed and the prototypes built. It was Tom Teagle's second home and a very important aspect of the company's philosophy.

It is sometimes difficult to sort fact from fiction when listening to stories about Tom Teagle. In many instances it was a case of "Well, I didn't see it but that was what I was told". One story involved an employee who asked if one of his relations could have a job. "Yes," said Tom, "he can have yours" and that was what happened – allegedly.

A newspaper article in 1971 spoke of Cornwall's industrial profile as a strange mixture of the new and the old, with the histories of some businesses going back to the Industrial Revolution. It spoke of some men working in converted barns while others were in glittering ultra-modern buildings. The graphic description was,

in fact, an introduction to a remarkable success story, that of Teagle Machinery Ltd. "The company had started," it said, "with a farmer, a cowshed and the farmer's inventive brain". It was an apt description for Tom Teagle, a man who is undoubtedly up there with the best of Cornish inventors – a man who deserves to be better-known and better-remembered. The article referred to the continuing involvement in experimental work and its further development by the erection of a new assembly building at Blackwater.

The UK's export success in Ireland so alarmed the Irish Government that it imposed a special customs duty to protect its own manufacturing companies but the tractor-mounted concrete mixers proved to be so popular that sales were unaffected. Clearly, Tom Teagle was delighted as he referred to it as just one of their niche markets across the world. Other successes were taking place in France, where an order had been placed for 4,000 broadcasters, and in Ohio where a local company had been licensed to manufacture the rotor-spreader for the United States market. In March 1971 there was another milestone when the company exported 1,150 machines – its highest figure to date. This included machines as varied as crop-drying fans for Iceland, fertilizer broadcasters for Australia and hedge-trimmers and mixers for France.

During the 1970s, life seemed to become far more complicated. Perhaps it was a reflection of the increasing bureaucracy arising from our membership of the Common Market. Undoubtedly, Brussels was having an increasing influence both on our farming industry and life in general. Certain countries seemed able to influence policies throughout Europe and we all became aware of such phrases as "food mountains" and "wine lakes". The failure to avoid over-production in certain commodities and the vacillations in the political world made it very difficult to plan ahead. A letter to Teagle customers in October 1972 refers to

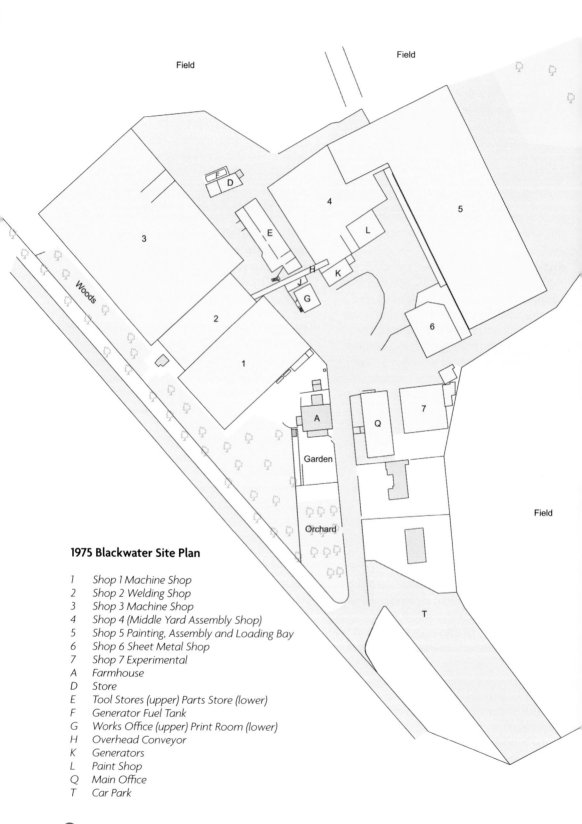

Field

Field

Field

Field

3

2

1

Woods

4

5

E

D

F

L

H

K

J

G

6

A

Q

7

Garden

Orchard

T

1975 Blackwater Site Plan

1	Shop 1 Machine Shop
2	Shop 2 Welding Shop
3	Shop 3 Machine Shop
4	Shop 4 (Middle Yard Assembly Shop)
5	Shop 5 Painting, Assembly and Loading Bay
6	Shop 6 Sheet Metal Shop
7	Shop 7 Experimental
A	Farmhouse
D	Store
E	Tool Stores (upper) Parts Store (lower)
F	Generator Fuel Tank
G	Works Office (upper) Print Room (lower)
H	Overhead Conveyor
K	Generators
L	Paint Shop
Q	Main Office
T	Car Park

the effect of joining the Common Market, as it was then called. In it, the likelihood of reduced costs was dismissed. It anticipated that food would become more expensive and that this, in turn, would increase the cost of wages. Furthermore, it anticipated that the price of steel would increase by about 15% to bring it in line with the other member countries. Value Added Tax was also on the horizon, a major change which was to be introduced on the 1st April 1973 – All Fools Day! The uncertainties were of great concern to everyone but for a manufacturing company with a large export turnover it must have been particularly worrying.

The company had an impressive display of products on show at the Drogheda Show in Ireland in June 1973. It was there as a part of the Armstrong Machinery Ltd stand. The location was not far from the River Boyne where the great battle took place in 1690 between James II and William of Orange which established this country as a Protestant nation. The Teagle display was unusual. It was a tower of machines including, of course, the Tipmix and Versatile which were proving to be so popular there.

Inflation was the scourge of the 1970s and an attempt by Prime Minister Edward Heath to control wages had bought the government into direct confrontation with the powerful coal mining unions. In 1973, the National Union of Mineworkers urged its members to work to rule and the country's coal stocks soon began to dwindle. To reduce electricity consumption, and thus conserve coal stocks, a series of measures was introduced including the "Three-Day Work Order". Like the rest of the UK manufacturing sector, Teagles was greatly affected by this restriction. It meant that from the 1st January until the 7th March commercial users of electricity were limited to three specified consecutive days' consumption each week. It hit all walks of life and became known as the "Three-Day Week".

1971 – SIMA, Paris

To minimise the effect of this restriction, Tom Teagle bought two huge diesel engines and a starting compressor which had previously been used on a warship. They were so big that they had to be started by using compressed air and, because of this, it was important to retain a sufficient amount for that use.

Alan Dell talked of the disruption caused by the loss of electrical power during this period and at other times when there was a break in supply. "It caused havoc at Tuckingmill until we installed a standby Rolls-Royce generator," he said. "It was brought over from the Blackwater factory and was often brought into use. We were able to carry on working while others were sitting in the dark. We always looked ahead and were prepared for that sort of problem."

John Teagle joined the company in 1975, after gaining an honours degree in agricultural engineering at the National College of Agricultural Engineering (later Silsoe College). By coincidence, directors Geoff Osborne, Duncan Wilson and John himself all received a gold medal for being student of the year, at a time when design was a pencil-and-paper job with Computer Aided Design just a distant dream.

At first, John worked alongside his father on the design of new products. It must have been a considerable challenge for this young man, fresh out of college. It was a pairing of the old and the new, or maybe a clash of the old and the new, because there was the occasional difficulty in the early days, perhaps best summed up by the old Cornish expression, "We belong to do it this way!"

In 1975, Teagle Machinery Ltd was among the 40 British firms exhibiting at the 49th Salon International de la Machine Agricole and at the 12th Salon International de l'Agriculture in Paris. The range on show covered almost every aspect of the agricultural industry. The companies were participating in a scheme supported by the British Overseas Trade Board in collaboration with the Agricultural Engineers Association and the British Agriculture Export Council.

During the mid-1970s Shop 6, the sheet metal shop, and Shop 5 were linked by an enclosed overhead conveyor, similar to the one that spanned the middle yard. Components, especially the concrete mixer drums, were fabricated and primed and then transported along this elevated tunnel to Shop 5 where the finishing coats of paint were applied. It remained in use until 2005 but by then it was no longer needed and was demolished.

Ron Hendry had previously worked for Beacon Garage at St Agnes and amongst his customers was Teagle Machinery Ltd, for whom he serviced the articulated lorries. He was aware that the pay there was much better than he was earning at the time so, in 1976, he left the garage and became a welder. He described the move as a "good decision".

Later, when work was a bit short and Ron was under notice to finish, Tom Teagle asked him to work overtime. Ron said, "I can't do that, Cap'n, I'm working out my notice". The next day Ron was removed from the payroll.

For the next few weeks he became a part of the experimental team and Tom paid his wages out of his own pocket. When the work situation improved he remained in that department. Ron describes Tom as a clever man but one who certainly liked discipline. "He tolerated an element of gaming around. He would pretend not to see it but if it was over the top then you would eventually get your comeuppance. Even so, he was never nasty and when you consider the pressure of running a company through good and bad times he treated us very well. I used to call him Cap'n and, by the way he used to look at me, I had the feeling that he didn't like it. Anyway, he always called me Rodney and he knew that wasn't my name so I suppose we were as bad as each other over that."

Later on Ron left to work elsewhere but after about a year he was tempted back and was pleased to return. He recommenced as a welder but when work was short again he was transferred to vehicle maintenance so his years as a mechanic were put to good use. That was where he remained for the next 20 years, until he retired in 2007.

In 1977 Austin Heyden of W & W A Heyden Machinery Ltd retired. The company had started in the early 1900s in a workshop at Plain-an-Gwarry, Redruth. Initially, it operated as a vehicle repair garage but more recently it had been carrying out specialised engineering work – precision engineering and heat treatment. From the 1950s onwards it was mainly carrying out work for Teagles. It employed about a dozen people and was an important factor in the Teagle supply chain. So important, in fact, that its imminent closure prompted the Teagle directors to buy the company.

Geoff Osborne joined Teagles as a design engineer in July 1978. He had previously worked for the Ford Motor Company, in the tractor division. In his own words, he was a Cornishman who wanted to return home. He reflected on the factors which he felt gave Teagles an edge, and high on the list was anticipating the needs of the agricultural industry. He said, "Many of us had strong links with the farming industry and our experience, together with feedback from our sales team, was fed into regular planning meetings where we decided future projects". At that time there were about 120 members of staff, a marked contrast to the huge international company where Geoff had previously worked. The Tuckingmill factory concentrated on trailers and muck-spreaders, the larger machinery, but being sited between Camborne and Redruth, in the industrial heart of Cornwall, the skills were available to produce the precision parts needed for the Blackwater factory: gears, (spur and bevel) and splines, gearbox components, hydraulic rams and PTO components. Fred Teagle ran the factory at Tuckingmill while Tom Teagle was in charge at Blackwater.

Geoff said, "Back then, the technology was much different. We had single and multi-spindle automatic lathes but Computer Numerical Control (CNC) machines hadn't even been thought of. Now, with the use of such machines, our efficiency and quality has improved tremendously. We had no choice but to introduce the changes if we wanted to continue to compete in what was an increasingly competitive world. During the Second World War anything that helped food production was in great demand and we were one of just a few who were designing and making agricultural machinery. By the time that I had joined the company the number had increased significantly. I can remember standing on the balcony at The Royal Smithfield Show at Earl's Court, a huge international event, and looking down at all the company banners but, since then, at least 30 UK manufacturing companies have disappeared. It's a terrible situation and a sad reflection on what has happened to the UK manufacturing sector."

Exports accounted for more than half of the turnover in 1978. Suddenly, however, it dropped, and Geoff Osborne reflected

1971 – Royal Smithfield Show

on the probable reasons. "We were exporting a considerable number of machines to France but then the market fell away. There were external factors like the political climate and the recession but there also seemed to be an anti-British feeling amongst the French farmers at that time. We also had some internal issues like quality which we knew that we had to address. The result of all these factors was a sudden and dramatic drop in exports. Of course, our home market also fluctuated but back then we didn't have area sales managers talking to dealers and pushing sales in the way we do today."

Roger Teagle, David Jones, John Teagle and Geoff Osborne at the 1978 Royal Smithfield Show

Brian Swallow and Tommy James at the 1978 Royal Smithfield Show

Robbie Field began working for the company in 1978 and was there for over 30 years. He began in the cut-off shop at Tuckingmill under Alan Dell and recalls that their biggest problem was in understanding each other – Robbie was a cockney and Alan a Cornishman. Robbie said, "It sounded like a foreign language to me and I was continually saying pardon. It was a time of considerable investment and the arrival of two lorry loads of large machines

Geoff Osborne (with the umbrella) enjoying a refreshing shower at the Royal Cornwall Show in 1979

certainly gave me the impression that I had joined a company which was going places."

A fail-safe braking mechanism certainly gained the praise of one user. It was described as the agricultural version of the engine driver's "deadman's handle," a braking system which had averted many accidents on the railways. With this device, the trailer could only be moved when it was properly coupled and the tractor engine was running. The unknown correspondent referred to it as a splendid idea and just another example of Cornish engineering skill being applied to a practical problem.

Describing the Blackwater site, the April 1978 *Livestock* publication suggested that the passing motorist might not be aware of the Teagle factory discreetly landscaped and unannounced just a few miles from the North Cornwall coast. He was correct, of course, but the same statement could be made about the folk who lived just a mile or so from the factory gate. They too, were unaware that behind the modest facade was an industrious engineering company which was respected both inside and outside the UK. The publication went on to say that the name of Teagle Machinery Ltd was synonymous with value for money. A large proportion of its products were destined for foreign parts and one of those products, it said, was the Dynacut Series S hedge-trimmer of which 2,000 had been sold since it was introduced three years earlier.

In October 1978 the Russians arrived. A party of 29 young agriculturists made the journey from Rostov in Yaroslavl Oblast for a ten-day exchange visit with Cornwall Young Farmers' Clubs. The itinerary included a ploughing match (horse and tractor) and a visit to Teagles where they were said to have shown great interest in the products. Fred Teagle took a somewhat different slant to the

The Teagle stand at the Royal Smithfield Show in 1979

newspapers as he recalled the visitors' reactions to what they saw. He said, "I was left with the distinct feeling that because Russian farms were so large compared to ours, they left with the impression that the tour had been a bit pointless.

Apart from anything else, they could not understand the logic of ploughing matches. Ploughing was simply an aspect of farming and they could not see the point of turning it into a competition."

1979 – Tom and Mary Teagle with their three sons, John, David and Fred, in front of the main office

The devastation caused by Dutch Elm Disease was the motivation for the introduction of a log splitter. It comprised a ram from a Dynacut together with some bits and pieces of steel from the scrap bin.

Within a day the prototype was in operation. It sold well and became an essential item for farmers who wanted to make one final use of their old trees.

One satisfied customer was so delighted that he wrote: "In twenty years of farming I have never before had such complete satisfaction with a new implement as I have experienced with your Hydrax log splitter. Whether knotted elm or twisted oak it is like the proverbial knife through butter. A 'must' for all who use wood burning appliances."

The
Hydrax Log Splitter

1980 – The Hydrax log splitter

Royal Smithfield Show 1980

In 1981, turnover was running at an all-time high but there was a problem just around the corner. The surge in the strength of the pound was presenting a real challenge for exporting companies. Teagles suddenly found that they were unable to compete in foreign markets, and orders that would usually come their way were being eagerly snapped up by local businesses in those export markets. This situation continued for some time and in 1983 it was still the

A visit by the National Dairy Queen must have turned a few heads in 1983 – she was there on a visit with Dorset YFC

high value of sterling that was presenting difficulties in the export market.

Grassland demonstrations were a common feature of agricultural life and in June 1982 Teagle representatives were at the national event at Stoneleigh in Warwickshire. A plot of about two acres was allocated to each company and they then had the opportunity to demonstrate just how good their machine really was. Potential agents and farmers could see the machines in use rather than just viewing them on a static display.

Running a company is a rewarding experience but most people can look back and identify a situation or period critical to their business's continued existence. For Teagle Machinery that year was 1984. It had become apparent that the government had decided that it was no longer prepared to continue its support for industry. Some would argue that this led to a situation where could the UK no longer produce sufficient food to feed itself and that this is why so much of our current

1983 – the SIMA exhibition in Paris

requirements are imported. It certainly had far-reaching ramifications and Fred Teagle identified 1984 as "the worst period in the company's history". The home market was hit as the supermarket-controlled retail food industry sucked in supplies from overseas and imposed harsh trading terms on its suppliers. Interest rates were also high and agriculture quotas were imposed as part of the government's measures to reduce its level of intervention in industry. Confidence in the agricultural industry slumped and few farmers were prepared to invest in new machinery. The result was devastating. Farmers were leaving the land at a rate of 6,000 per year, demand for farm machinery fell by over 40% and many manufacturers and dealers went to the wall. At Teagles, the level of sales slumped. Its turnover was halved and there seemed to be no avenue through which new business would come. Whether or not you agree with the measures being taken by Margaret Thatcher and her Conservative government it was unquestionably the end of an era for British manufacturing. Companies, not just in agriculture, which

failed to face up to that fact either closed or were forced into liquidation. Teagles had been in existence for over forty years and, whilst this was a huge challenge, the directors were not about to roll over and give in to this external threat. Decisive action was needed and that did not include tinkering around the edges. Work at Tuckingmill was halted and all production concentrated at the Blackwater site. For many it was a sad day. Tuckingmill was where they had worked and formed friendships and to watch the site being dismantled and the machines sold was not something which they had expected. Some men transferred to Blackwater, including the works manager Bob Fowler, but not all could be accommodated and they left to try to find work elsewhere.

The surplus machinery at Tuckingmill was auctioned on site by M Isaacs & Son – at "Tucking Mill, Cambourne" (sic). We can assume that Tuesday the 11th September 1984 was a long day as the sales inventory included almost 400 machines and pieces of equipment that

Royal Smithfield Show 1984

went under the auctioneer's hammer. Apart from that, it must have taken a good few hours to decide what to sell and what to keep. Within the auction catalogue was an invitation for offers for the 10.5 acre freehold site. In this case, the local company of Fox & Sons had spelt Camborne correctly!

With the Tuckingmill closure the disadvantages of running a multi-site company were removed. Apart from Heyden's small unit at Redruth, and one small workshop still in use at Tuckingmill, work was now concentrated at Blackwater. No longer would there be the duplication of overheads nor the problems and costs attached to inter-site communication and transportation.

Despite the dreadful trading conditions the directors held their nerve. Indeed, they not only kept the company together but continued with an ambitious investment programme including a bold computerisation plan. The pressures at this time must have been immense but the

measures paid off and the result was the transformation of Teagle Machinery Ltd into a company which would grow and compete with the best in the world. Fred Teagle described the resultant organisation as lean, mean and fully computerised. Everything from design to manufacture to despatch was linked by computer. It was a huge investment but one that ultimately reaped benefits.

Ron Hendry was in the experimental section when Tom Teagle told him to put a slow bend on a piece of 25mm by 25mm RHS. Ron said, "It was 6mm thick and I tried but I couldn't move it. He came over, pushed me out of the way and just pulled it into the shape he wanted. He was a strong chap." Others have spoken of Tom's great strength and there are stories of him carrying a hundredweight-and-a-half (75kg) bag of corn up into the granary.

No factory would be complete without its share of banter in fact, it often helps to "oil the wheels" of harmony. During the interviews for this book there have been many stories, some printable, others not. One involved Fred Boaden who was clearly "vertically challenged". He was said to be "too short to piss in a pit". Clearly, though, some of the work was a bit repetitive and it is understandable that something was needed to relieve the boredom.

At Tuckingmill, too, there was the usual amount of leg-pulling, including the time when someone's bicycle was hoisted up and tied to a roof beam. The bemused chap eventually gave up looking for it and walked home. The next day he complained that it had been stolen but when they went to check, it had been lowered and was back in its usual place. Another chap was ex-army and always used his tin cup at crib time. The tea was poured as usual but when he raised it up to take a slurp he found that it had been screwed to the table. A young Gary Richards was warned by his father that he would have to watch out for all the usual tricks, like being sent for a long weight (wait) or for a wire-netting wheelbarrow to wheel away the smoke. It was all part of the initiation process for both the engineering and construction industries.

Sometime in the 1980s, the men decided to form a cricket team. They played for various clubs at the weekends and thought that a Teagle team with occasional games against other organisations would be good. Alan Dell was tasked with trying to obtain the equipment and he walked into a board meeting and asked if the company would help with the cost of the kit. He was a bit taken aback, and a tad embarrassed, when Tom Teagle turned to him and said, "No, the company won't contribute". He wished that he hadn't asked but that changed when Tom said, "I will, though, what do you want?" He was true to his word and before long they had everything they needed. Alan said, "He must have been a bit interested because he used to wander up to watch us practise".

Royal Smithfield Show 1985

The
Bale Shredders

1985 – The Lightning – later named the Tomahawk 100 bale shredder

During the 1980s, farmers were looking for a machine which would break apart, chop and bed bales. Cattle and sheep had problems with long silage and feeding in enclosed areas was monotonous work. Apart from that, hay and straw had become expensive and some very influential reports had suggested that economies could be made by chopping it into short lengths. In fact, the evidence was of a one-third saving when used for bedding.

As a result of this research, the Lightning small bale shredder was developed. It would not only deal with farm produce but could also chop paper, plastics and other materials, opening up its potential for diversification. As it turned out, however, there was no large take-up by other sectors but within the farming community it proved to be a winner and the forerunner of a large number of similar machines produced under the Teagle banner.

Tom Teagle was having problems with his hips. The pain was hard to bear and his mobility was severely affected. It was not something that he could put up with for long and he was soon booked in for two hip replacements. One was successful but the other needed a repeat operation and, from then on, he walked with the aid of a stick. He was seldom seen without it and on one occasion Dick Littlejohns and John Veall were in the production office when they saw him approach a bale shredder which was on a working test. It was attached to a tractor positioned on the island. They were aware that it was jammed and they watched as Tom tried to clear it – with his stick. Dick said, "He lifted the outlet flap and began poking it. I can't remember whether or not he cleared it but when he pulled out his stick all that remained was a piece about a foot long: the machine had chewed off the rest. He just stood there with a perplexed look on his face. We couldn't stop laughing."

Fred Teagle also remembered a straw shredder test in the orchard when the outlet chute was taken off and the chopped straw shot up towards the sky. The wind blew it across the buildings and over Fred's house – they were picking up bits of straw for weeks.

With the increase in size and power of tractors came the push for larger bales. The next challenge for the design team was to produce a shredder which could deal not only with the increased size but also the change in shape. It was the era of the big round bales. Various prototypes of the shredder were produced and this photograph shows the earliest with its vertical drum. It did the job but there were loading difficulties. How much easier it would be if the drum could be tilted to the rear, but the concept was that it was a vertical-feed machine with the bale forced onto the cutters by gravity. In the vertical model this was no problem but by tilting it, the downward movement of the

1987 – Prototype big round bale shredder

The five-foot diameter sloping-drum bale shredder first appeared at the Royal Smithfield Show in 1987

1989 – The Tomahawk 500 bale straw shredder

1992 – The Tomahawk 5000 silage feeder

Northern Sales Area Manager Peter Hagan at the Highland Show with the Royal Highland 1992 silver medal for new implements

bale was reduced. There was an optimum angle and once this was found it could be worked to advantage by varying that angle to increase or decrease the feed rate. The machine was a winner and the development of this range of bale shredders was a huge step forward. Having begun with a machine designed around the traditional small bales, "boys' bales" as Geoff Osborne calls them, Teagles had produced a machine which could evolve as bales increased in size and even changed in shape. It was, and still is, the company's major product line.

In 1988 the full range of shredders were titled Tomahawk, a name which has become synonymous with quality bedding and feeding machinery ever since. It was a product which opened up new markets across the world.

In 1989 a legal problem arose when a rival company claimed that their patent had been infringed. Claims and counterclaims led to Fred and Dinah Teagle spending a considerable amount of time in European university libraries undertaking a "prior art" search (trying to discover who had manufactured the first such machine). The research paid off. Similar machines to the patented one had been produced in Italy and Denmark and this opened the door to continue making them for world markets.

Options to make the machine more universal were soon available – chutes were added to deliver straw at high level, low level, around corners, through tubes, or even into rows on the ground. Extended drums could be fitted to suit bales of differing size, all done to meet customers' particular requirements.

The shredder had become such an indispensable item that pressure was growing to extend its use to feed silage. The problem was designing rotors and housings which would not clog when dealing with such a soggy material. Eventually, in 1991, a version was produced which could handle it. The Tomahawk 4000 and 5000 silage feeder's first outing was at Grassland South West where it was the only machine on the market able to discharge round bale silage along feed passages, into feed mangers or to stock in the fields. It attracted interest from 12 countries.

1993 – The Tomahawk 5050 model processing silage

As with any product, considerable investment was necessary for every new development both in terms of design and tooling but adapting to change was very important and soon the 404, 505, 4040 and 5050 models came on stream and took their place in this very important range in 1993.

1994 – The Tomahawk 5050 feeder-bedders which won the coveted silver medal at the Royal Show. Left to right: Mike Fairey (TSB Sponsors), Fred Teagle (Teagle Managing Director), Gillian Shephard (Minister of Agriculture) and John Teagle (Teagle Sales Director).

There was yet another award for the Tomahawk silage feeder in 1992. On this occasion it was the prestigious Silver Medal from the Royal Agricultural Society of England, Britain's premier award for new products for the agriculture industry. Awarded annually, it takes account of new features and

1994 – The Tomahawk 5080 feeder-bedder

1997 – Differing screens for Tomahawk straw mills

2007 – The T505ME electric drive Tomahawk produced mainly for the European market

outstanding benefits in terms of functions and performance.

The ever-increasing size of bales meant further changes to the range and the six-foot diameter Tomahawk 606 and 6060 were introduced, mainly for the export market.

The advent of the big rectangular bales brought another necessary change and the need to spend more time at the proverbial drawing-board. In 1992, Teagles began a programme of research and development to deal with this innovation and over the next few years many prototypes were produced. While this was going on, however, it was decided to make a trailed five-foot machine with an eight-foot extended drum. The 508 and 5080 models worked well. They sold well in the home market and some were exported, albeit in small numbers.

The evolutionary process ticked on and the next item that came on stream, in 1997, was the Tomahawk Straw Mill. This machine enabled the farmer to produce very fine chopped straw for use as cattle feed. Chop lengths could be selected by changing the sieves so that straw as short as 10mm could be produced.

Diversity is a great feature and the potential to use such a machine in an industrial situation was recognised. The T505ME electric-motor-driven version included power sensors to vary the speed of the drum as the load on the rotor changed.

The Box-Type Machines

The Tomahawk 700 never moved to the production stage but its features were the basis for the models which followed and by 1998 the 808MF box-type shredder was on the market. It had twin cross beaters which were driven by a 90° gearbox mounted on the side panel.

The following year, the 8080TC with twin chutes was considered so innovative that it won the Technical Award from the Royal Highland Agricultural Association of Scotland. Its versatility had caught the judges' eye and if you were around at the time, and you fancied taking one home, you could have towed it away for £10,995.

A larger capacity box-type shredder was produced in 2000. The 9090 had all the features of its smaller cousin but was available for customers who needed a larger output.

The dual-chop feeder version was an important breakthrough. It could deliver finely chopped or full length straw controlled by the flick of a switch in the tractor cab. The universal swivel chute model enabled the operator to bed or feed on either side of the machine by using the directional outlet.

1992 – The prototype Tomahawk 700 box-type shredder

1998 – The Tomahawk 808MF bedder

1999 – The Tomahawk 8080TC twin-chute bedder

2000 – The Tomahawk 9090 feeder-bedder

BELOW: 2002 – The Tomahawk 808S mounted bedder – a more manoeuvrable model than the trailed version

2006 – The Tomahawk 8080SC feeder-bedder with sloping chute

2006 – A self-propelled Tomahawk in New Zealand

2009 – The Tomahawk 8080WB feeder-bedder

2010 – The Tomahawk 1010 feeder-bedder

2012 – The relaunched extensively modified Tomahawk range – the Flow-Plus – T8100 standard and T8150 dual-chop and the T8500 standard wide-body and T8550 dual-chop wide-body models

As balers and tractors continued to increase in size so did the demand for larger shredding machines and this led to the introduction of the 8080WB wide-body model.

It seemed that everything was getting bigger, but whereas it had previously been possible to simply increase the dimensions, the Tomahawk 1010 required a completely new design. It was a very large capacity version which had the facility of optional weigh-cell technology. Most are exported to North America but a considerable number go to Europe and the Far East.

By 2012 the Tomahawk round bale shredder was in its third decade and in need of updating. It was extensively redesigned, modern decals were applied and the new models were launched for the 2012/13 season. Initially the drums were fitted with extensions as an accessory but within a short time a new model with a 2.5-metre drum with extra supports was introduced. This version was able to chop or mill the largest straw bales produced.

Such was the impact of the Tomahawk range on the industry that in January 2013 *The Farmers' Guardian* featured it in its Hot 50, referring to it as: "Widely recognised as the industry standard for bale feeding and bedding machines".

2014 – Tomahawk working in Bolivia

2014 – Tomahawk being delivered to a Polish customer

2012 – The extended-drum Tomahawk 505XLM mill

The Telehawk Feeder-Bedder

The 2014 Telehawk feeder-bedders

The Telehawk feeder-bedder brings the story right up to the present time with a machine which has all the attributes of its predecessors but with features which greatly increase the benefit to the farmer.

It is mounted on a telescopic loader and processes both round and rectangular bales. It is self-loading and its rotating chute can deliver straw across a 280° arc. The controls, too, are more advanced with Bluetooth wireless control and sensors which optimise the processing speed.

The bale shredders are still the company's main product though that would not have been the case but for a critical decision back in the early 1980s. John Teagle recalled that the directors had to decide whether to concentrate on their range of hedge-trimmers or to develop and produce a bale shredder.

The benefits of chopped straw and silage were being trumpeted and with only one UK competitor producing bale shredders it was decided that this was the product of the future. The company has now been producing versions of this machine for thirty years and such is the continued demand that there is no sign that production will diminish in the foreseeable future.

Brian Hutchins worked at the Blackwater factory for almost 50 years and during that time he saw many changes. He said, "In the early days you ate your dinner at your work place – you found an old drum to sit on and tucked in to whatever you had brought".

Ron Hendry said, "Before we had a canteen it was not unusual to see a pile of empty baked bean tins in the workshop. They built up over a few days before someone would eventually decide to dump them. For a bit of fun, Brian Watts tack-welded a row of about 15 of them to a flail machine part. Anyway, the part arrived in front of me and I decided to play along with it. I stick-welded them and pushed it along to the next chap – Russell Fowler. He said, 'What's this then?' and I walked away laughing. Anyway, Russell welded the part with all the bean cans still in place. The foreman arrived and had a go at Russell but he just said, 'Well, I thought they were a part of it!' I was almost sent home for that but I managed to get away with it."

Many have described Russell Fowler and Ron Hendry as outstanding characters whose camaraderie and fun helped maintain a happy spirit in the factory. According to Robbie Field it left a bit of a hole when Russell retired.

Tom Teagle was undoubtedly a clever man who was always coming up with good ideas, sometimes at night. If the eureka moment came, then he would get out of bed, put on his overalls and head off down to the workshop.

It was not unusual for him to ask someone to make "something like this" and he would bend his arm to indicate what shape he wanted. He was quick to say if it was wrong, as when someone brought back a piece of work with the holes in a different position from what he wanted. He looked at it and said, "You were lucky there, you nearly missed the steel". On the other hand, he was equally quick to give praise if it was just what he wanted.

On one occasion Tom handed someone a short piece of bar and asked him to drill a hole in it. Having watched him walk away the guy scratched his head and told his colleague what he had been told to do. Eventually, he asked Tom where he wanted the hole and how big it had to be. Tom's response was short and to the point: "If I'd wanted it in a certain place I would have said – just drill a hole". The piece of work was duly handed over and the guy must have wondered what technical role his piece of work was going to play. Tom casually threaded a piece of rope through it, tied a knot and tossed it over the loaded lorry. He simply wanted a weight on the end of the rope.

Former employee Gordon Bennetts recalled Mr Teagle and his stick. He said, "He often went up to someone on a Friday afternoon, pointed his stick at them, and said, 'We'll carry on with such and such tomorrow morning'. It became a game and if you didn't want to work on a Saturday you avoided him all Friday afternoon."

His stick would often be missing. Someone would hide it down the open end of a steel tube or behind something. He had a number of them and would simply wander off to find another. Every so often something would be moved and a bundle of sticks would tumble out. Ron reckoned that he had his suspicions but he never knew for sure who had hidden them. The chalk provided for marking the work was hard and glassy and Tom hated using it so he had his own – the ordinary blackboard type. One day, Ron Hendry removed it from his bench and replaced it with the standard issue. After spending some time searching for his chalk, Tom picked up the company-issue piece and threw it the length of the workshop. Ron said, "I reckon he knew who swopped it but he didn't say anything. He did have a sense of humour but he would always look down and smile to try and disguise his reaction. He wasn't one to forget, either. There was an occasion when a chap was spouting off about the Cornish. Tom looked at him over the top of his glasses but didn't say a word. At the end of the day he wandered over and told him that his work was well below the standard expected in Cornwall and that he should start again."

Gordon Bennetts said, "Tom Teagle expected us to work hard but he knew what was going on and sometimes you could detect a faint smile on his face. He was realistic enough to realise that we couldn't work every minute of the day and I remember that when he walked into a workshop he would slam the door and for the first six or seven paces he would look down at the floor. There was a good camaraderie and we even had a bit of sport after work: cricket, football, and before I joined there was even a rugby team. The work was hard but I enjoyed working for him and even after he had died the company carried on in much the same way. I appreciated the way we were treated, they even sent some of us to the Royal Cornwall Show and paid for our meals."

During the 1970s and 1980s Tom Teagle was less involved in running the company. The management was left in the capable hands of his three sons and his wife, Mary, who was determined to remain involved as long as she was able. Tom was still on the scene, however, ready with ideas and suggestions based on a lifetime of experience. It must have been difficult for him. After all, he had given life to this embryonic business and now he was entrusting it to others. He must have known, however, that it would only flourish if the next generation was allowed to take the reins. In any event, it left him with more time to spend on what he most enjoyed and, even in his advancing years, he continued to work at his drawing board, striving to solve problems and come up with some new labour-saving ideas.

> ## SURPRISING WHAT AN INDEPENDENT CAN DO!
> *From an article published in a 1984 S.E. England N.F.U. Journal,*
>
> "Situated only 40 miles from Lands End" is how one article about the company began. It went on to report, "Teagle Machinery is one of the remaining family-owned agricultural machinery manufacturing companies not taken over by large conglomerates". It identified the invention of the potato planter as the start of the company and mentioned that it was commandeered by the Ministry of Agriculture for use by war agricultural committees. It also listed other inventions including a 49cc two-stroke engine which was cheaper, more efficient and more reliable than others available at that time. It added, "It was no mean feat for a self-taught engineer leading a small company working in converted farm buildings and using basic engineering machinery".

There were two very different sides to Mary Teagle, according to Ron Hendry. "In the office she was a real tiger. She ruled her world – sometimes with the proverbial rod of iron. That was one side of her but when she was with her grandchildren, or in the garden with her bees, she was an entirely different person – a much gentler soul."

Mary hated being let down and if anyone failed to do what they promised, they would feel the sharp edge of her tongue. Dick Littlejohns has vivid memories of her and of catching her on a bad day when she was clearly not in the mood for conversation. "But," he said, "she was the real driving force. She ran the office and even managed to help out in the parts stores. I've seen her struggling up across the yard with some weighty items. I've even offered to carry them for her but she always said that she could manage."

The 1985 Royal Smithfield Show

An article in the January 1985 edition of *Power Farming* suggested that there had been a step-change in the quality of machines leaving the factory gate. It stated, "Today's machines are designed and built on a par, both in quality and value, with any other maker of similar products". John Teagle acknowledged this. He said that there had been a recognition that they needed to tighten up on the specifications. Up until then, the machines had been built to a predetermined figure which they knew would sell, but there had been a growing awareness that the future lay in selling on quality.

Sometime in the mid-1980s Tom Teagle suffered a heart attack. More attacks followed and he received strict orders that he was to "take it easy". No one who knew him imagined that it would be easy. The family considered placing him under "house arrest" but they were aware that the stress of incarceration would be greater than letting him don his overalls and continue as normal – it was exactly what happened. He ignored all the warnings and continued to live out his remaining time doing what he loved – sitting at his drawing board and pottering around in his workshop.

By 1985 the Tuckingmill site was still unsold. The workers of the original Bickford Smith Company, ICI, and Teagles had deserted it but one small group of workers remained.

Gary Richards had been handed some leaflets on CNC lathes and told that the company was thinking of buying one. It was to be installed in Shop 5 at Tuckingmill and would be a part of the W & W A Heyden section. A trip to London with Fred Teagle followed and in due course the new machine arrived. The Tuckingmill site was still busy with equipment being stripped out and taken to Blackwater but once that was done it became much quieter, with only Gary and two colleagues occupying the huge site. It must have seemed like a ghost town. That situation prevailed for the next five or six years during which time the small team produced precision work for use at the Blackwater factory and for other local engineering companies. From time to time, Tom Teagle paid them a visit and on one occasion he was intrigued as he stood watching Gary setting the new CNC lathe. Seemingly unconvinced at the wisdom of installing such a machine, Tom commented that he could do the same job on his machine at Blackwater. Gary asked him how long it would take and Tom replied that he reckoned that he could "knock one out" in about an hour. "How long does it take you?" he asked and when Gary said, "Five-and-a-half minutes" he nodded and said, "I can see why we bought it".

The first CNC lathe was installed at Tuckingmill in 1985

1985 – Tuckingmill Shops 1A, 1 and 2 looking south

Pendarves Street

N

The Tuckingmill site plan in 1987

1A   Material Storage and Machine Shop
1   Machine Shop
2   Assembly Shop
3   Heat Treatment
5   Precision Machine Shop
7   Assembly Shop

In 1985, Tom Teagle was involved in a car accident when a driver heading towards him lost control of his vehicle. It was not a huge collision, more of a glancing blow, but it meant a 12-day stay in hospital and a considerable period of convalescence. By then, Tom had handed over control of the company to his sons so his time away from the factory had no detrimental effect on the business but it was a bad experience for someone in his mid-70s and a particularly testing time for this hitherto dynamic engineer.

Tom's day-to-day involvement was now limited to providing a few ideas but it is difficult to imagine this active man sitting back and letting the world go by. Of course, he did not! His spare time was taken up with the study of all sorts of subjects including microbiology and nuclear physics which, he said, left him with no end of interesting studies and research. It leaves us wondering what he could have invented if he had followed this path earlier in life. Shortly before his death he wrote to the newspapers saying that he had acquired a considerable knowledge on the subject, sufficient to challenge the enormous spending on a local hot-rocks project being undertaken at that time. The rather disparaging letter contained a technical denial of the idea which he summarised by saying, "Before another granite-boring

The Royal Smithfield Show in 1986

jamboree is considered, boring costs will have to be slashed by 90%, technology increased twenty-fold and oil rise to 600 dollars a barrel".

With the daily pressure of business lifted, he had plenty of time for study and for a few campaigns. Letting go of the company reins, however, did not reduce his concerns for the financial fortunes of the agricultural industry or, indeed, the country, and he was scathing about the Chancellor's decision to raise the bank rate at a time when primary industries needed all the help they could get to play their part in reducing the national trading deficit. In one letter he wrote, "I never trust a politician of any colour, I do not vote so I do not worry. I have more work than I shall ever accomplish."

Duncan Wilson's first contact with the company was as a student, in 1987. He spent his work-experience time in various departments including the drawing office which he would eventually head. He returned to college to complete his course and it was not until he telephoned Geoff Osborne for a reference that he renewed his acquaintance. Geoff's response was to ask him to hold on a minute and, a few moments later, Duncan was offered a job as a design engineer. So began his career working for a medium-size farm machinery company situated in, for him, far-off Cornwall.

Teagles have provided industry-based work-placements for many students. Some, like Duncan, returned to work for the company while others have been employed at JCB, John Deere and similar large organisations. The more recent have been from Harper Adams University. Students from there with an agricultural background can spend 12 months in industry whereas those with no agricultural experience have to split their time between farming and industry.

Ken Crago worked for the company from the early 1950s. He was the design

1987 – Fred Teagle, John Teagle, Dinah Teagle, Amanda Woodley, Mark Hood, unknown, Paul Bache, Duncan Wilson, Geoff Osborne – the team at the Royal Smithfield Show

engineer involved in the design, testing and everything associated with the development of new products. When he retired in the late 1980s Geoff Osborne took over his role.

In 1989, the installation of a CAD (Computer Aided Design) system was under way. New skills were needed and an extensive training programme was necessary to ensure a smooth transition. The implementation totally changed the production process and made possible the introduction of computer-controlled cutting, bending and turning machines to the factory floor. Complicated shapes could be cut and folded more accurately, producing components which required far less work at the finishing or fettling stage. In simple terms, this meant that if you could draw it on the computer then you could make it from the digital information. About three years later, the system was upgraded to a full-blown three-dimensional version which could not only show how components would look but would also determine whether or not they could withstand the stress and strains to which they would eventually be subjected. Using this information, machines could be designed to be lighter, stronger and more attractive. In addition, a reasonably accurate estimate of the cost could be made to determine whether the machine would be viable in the market place.

Geoff Osborne said, "Before CAD there were lots of great ideas and even prototypes which never made it into production. Even if they did progress to the shop floor they had to be modified many times. Now, with the aid of CAD, we can determine whether everything fits together before you cut the first bit of steel."

A bit closer to home – the Royal Cornwall Show in 1988

Death of the Inventor
(Mernans an Deviser)

Tom Teagle's death marked the end of an era. This larger-than-life character had devoted his life to the company and it would now have to continue without him.

His death was unexpected: it took place when the family was representing the company in London at the Royal Smithfield Show. The newspapers included many reports about this well-respected inventor and businessman. Family and friends, too, added their recollections of this giant of a man who had contributed so much to Cornish industry. David Teagle referred to his father as an ideas man rather than a businessman: one who had allowed his hobby to take over his life. To Geoff Osborne he was a colourful character and, in many ways, a man before his time.

As the news of Tom's death spread through the factory it was greeted with a mixture of sorrow and concern. They mourned the man who had built the company and provided so many families with a livelihood, but they also feared that his death would bring about great change, maybe even the disposal of the company. Robbie Field recalled the speculation at the time. He said, "We were concerned at what it would mean to our jobs but we took comfort from the fact that Mrs Teagle was still involved. In many ways she was as big a part of the company as her husband and, as the situation developed, it became clear that the business would continue as it always had."

Many of the longer-term employees attended Tom's funeral, which was held at St Columb Major Church, in the locality of his birth.

Because of Tom's failing health he had taken a back seat in the day-to-day running of the company, so his death did not make as much difference to the business as it might otherwise have done. Fred Teagle had been at the helm for some time and the situation was now formalised as he became managing director.

It is with regret that we have to advise you that

William Thomas (Tom) Teagle

Founder and Former Chairman and Managing Director of Teagle Machinery Limited, died suddenly at his home on Wednesday 6th December 1989.

The Funeral was held at St. Columb Major Parish Church on Saturday 9th December 1989

Donations to the British Heart Foundation in lieu of flowers Teagle Machinery Limited, Blackwater, Truro, Cornwall.

Dealers and Agents

The use of agents to promote and sell its machinery was an essential part of the company's success. One such business was Gwili Jones and Sons of Carmarthen and in her book *Gwili Jones and Sons – A Brief History*, Eileen Jones wrote, "Teagle machinery sold really well: we must have sold hundreds of the great little aptly named Versatile broadcaster, SCM elevators and Silver and Golden Bullet Tracuts. All good machines and sensibly priced." She said that Gwili clearly remembered the first deal he made with the late Tom Teagle, a man "whose inventive genius was highly regarded in the trade". She recalled that the conversation was from a Peniel telephone kiosk and was along these lines:
Gwili: "Will you supply me with new machinery?"
Tom: "Will you guarantee to pay me?"
Gwili: "I'll pay you now, upfront, if you want".
Tom: "No, you pay me when you get the machines".
She goes on to say, "And so it was, the beginning of an ongoing relationship between our two companies that has lasted up until the present day. It gave us enormous pleasure to welcome Mary Teagle, her son Fred and his wife Dinah to our celebratory Open Day at Hafod on the 1st May 1997 – on Gwili's 70th birthday. Fred flew them to Swansea airport in his private plane."

Fred recalled an occasion when Gwili Jones asked him to demonstrate a Matchless mower in a field which Gwili had been contracted to cut. Apparently, there were a few potential customers who wanted to see it in action but by the time that he had finished the field no one had turned up to see it working. "Never mind," said Gwili, "just pop down and cut the other one and they'll soon be here". Apparently two or three chaps did turn up to see it in action but,

Mary Teagle, Fred and Dinah in conversation with Eileen Jones at the Open Day at Hafod

by then, Gwili had had two fields cut, free of charge! Nevertheless, He went on to sell many Matchless mowers over the years.

In the same book by Eileen Jones was an article about Tom James, Teagle's demonstrator/driver. She wrote, "He turned up regularly, delivering small machines such as the Tipmix and Versatile broadcaster. Mrs Teagle was in charge of transport and was of the opinion that a representative calling on dealers did not need a swish car – a pick-up, delivering the goods at the same time, made far more business sense. Tom James was a lovely, kind person, always cheerful and smiling, with white, strong, wavy hair and a most pronounced Devon accent [Cornish actually, Mrs Jones]."

1960 – Tom James' Thames demonstration vehicle 815 HAF waiting for the "off"

The 1989 Royal Show with John Teagle, Ian Arnold, driver, Peter Hagan, Nothern Area Manager and Geoff Osborne hiding behind a pair of shades and beard!

Geoff Osborne contributed these few paragraphs on Teagle's dealer network. "In the early days, the agricultural engineering industry sold machines to farmers through a multitude of dealerships, each operating over a radius of perhaps no more than 10 miles. Farm sizes were small by today's standards, thus the number of customers to be serviced was huge. Transport and communications, although improving steadily, were a drawback and local businesses thrived in that environment. The vast majority of dealers were single outlets and were usually either small companies or family enterprises. It was against this background that Teagle's business grew steadily.

Several of the early dealers have grown with time and remain a strong force in the Teagle network – Gwili Jones (mentioned previously) and Central Garage at Leedstown are prime examples. Ken Hall founded Central Garage in 1958, so he is a relative newcomer compared to his Welsh counterpart. In spite of their age difference however, the two companies have many similarities – which you would expect in a family-run organisation. Digressing slightly, at the tender age of 19, Ken fell in love with a Jaguar car and

today his collection is in the high teens, with eleven taxed and ready to go onto the road. People (including one or two Teagle customers) come from all over the world to see Ken's amazing collection. Fortunately, his wife, Hazel, is also besotted by Jaguars!

Back to machinery, several more recent additions to the Teagle fold are again family-owned and run businesses. Harold Johns, covers a large part of South-East Wales from modern premises set in the valley above Tintern. Harold (once described as 'The Salt of the Earth') and his small team, have successfully grown his Teagle business over the last 20 years to become a major player in the South-West territory. His life however is not easy – someone once asked the question 'What is the difference between a terrorist and a Welsh farmer?' – answer 'You can negotiate with a terrorist!' Working with Huw Brown, salesman at Harold Johns, Teagles Area Manager Mike Sanders stepped backwards into a slurry pool, right up to his waist, earning himself the nickname 'Swampy'.

Young businesses can be born when big ones fall apart. Way up in North Wales, and covering most of the UK, Burgess, a large multi-branch outlet, went into liquidation leaving sales staff with a large customer base at their finger tips, but with no employer and no product to sell. Answer: – set up your own business – so PGF Agri and Harrison Machinery were conceived, with Dylan Williams and Eric Harrison seeing their businesses thrive.

Over the years, farming has changed, together with businesses in general. Everything has grown bigger – farms are larger (and fewer), communications and transport more efficient and of course machinery has got bigger. The combination of all these factors has led to the growth of large (and sometimes enormous) multi-branch outlets. Ernest Doe has grown from a blacksmith's's shop in the late 1890s to a 19-branch operation stretching from Suffolk down to Sussex. In Scotland, Sellars Agriculture has branches stretching from Edinburgh to Elgin, whilst in the West, Morris Corfield extend from Leominster to Tarvin, and, more recently, in the South, Farols branches extend between Hinkley and Midhurst. Such names feature highly in the list of Teagle stockists and this is a reflection of the fact that Teagle has also grown, along with the rest of the industry."

1990 – The first Farley plasma cutter installed

The 1990s

In January 1990 a group of Japanese businessmen visited the factory. Their interest in the range of products began at the Royal Smithfield Show but no one really expected that it would be converted into a sale. They were from Hokkai Ford Tractors, tractor and agricultural machinery importer, and they were so impressed with the Tomahawk 500 bale shredder that they placed an order for 14. Japan was not one of Teagle's traditional markets and the perception was that Japanese technology was far in advance of our own. That was certainly so in the motor industry but it

transpired that it was not the case with their agricultural machinery manufacturers. In February of the following year the first consignment was loaded into a container for the long sea voyage to Japan. The shredder's prime purpose was for silage and hay but in Japan it would be used for rice. Teagle machines were in use in many countries across the world and now Japan was added to the long list.

With the CAD system now firmly in place it was possible to introduce a new family of machines to the workplace and in the spring of 1990, an Australian Farley plasma cutter arrived. Once in use it was difficult

Summer 1990 – An aerial view of the Blackwater factory

Three of the five latest Esprit plasma cutters in action

to imagine life without it. Out went the old guillotines and the new machine produced a quality of cut which removed the need for so much grinding and shaping. This, of course, greatly increased efficiency and without this new technology the company would have been unable to compete. Another benefit was the dramatic reduction in the amount of waste steel. The nine-metre by two-metre machine was programmed to use the most economical cutting pattern and so reduce the pile of scrap steel piled up outside the door.

The Esprit Viper plasma cutter in use

Such was the benefit derived from the plasma cutter that by 2002 a fourth such machine had been installed. In 2008, the initial machine had come to the end of its working life and the company had no hesitation in replacing it. By 2014 there were five in use – all fully occupied and all British made.

Teagles truly became a one-site business in 1990 when the handful of staff at Tuckingmill transferred to Blackwater. They were followed within a few months by the Heyden employees from the Redruth workshop and all of them were located in Shop 7. The Heyden workshop site at Plain-an-Gwarry was sold for housing, thus ending an engineering presence there which had lasted for about 100 years.

One of the last employees at Tuckingmill was Gary Richards who, following the transfer, became the foreman of Shop 7. It was interesting to hear him use both metric and imperial measurement in the same sentence but, as he explained, there were still a few elderly English machines in use

Fred and Dinah Teagle at the 1992 Royal Smithfield Show – order book at the ready

and it would not have been cost-effective to metricate them.

The old photographs and news items in the *West Briton and Royal Cornwall Gazette* are always popular with those of us who like to reminisce and reflect on times past. On the 25th April 1991 there was a superb photograph of Mullion fishermen but it was

The Princess Royal at the 1993 Royal Smithfield Show discussing the attributes of the Tomahawk range of machines with Fred Teagle

the news item from 50 years ago that caught our eye. It related, of course, to 1941 and referred to the Teagle machine which had transformed potato planting and was doing the same amount of work in one day as 30 to 40 men using old-fashioned methods. This simple statement probably sums up Tom Teagle's ethos and his endless drive to find a better way of doing things.

A feature by Peter Forde in the *South West Farmer* in July 1993 suggests that if there was one major factor in the continuing wellbeing of Teagle Machinery Ltd it was the ability to anticipate the needs of an ever-evolving farming industry. It seems like a good observation, as relevant today as when Tom made the first cart. The article also referred to the expertise required to make the implement to do the job without headache or hassle, the need to make it reliable and long-living and the essential requirement to provide value for money. Put like that it sounds easy but we are left to wonder what the modern-day *Dragon's Den* would have made of this Cornish farmer who had the temerity to enter their world with some hair-brained idea about making a few farm machines. Perhaps they would have been persuaded by his enthusiasm and common sense or maybe, just maybe, he would have been a tad too forthright for their liking. In 1994, Teagles exhibited at the Royal Welsh

Show for the first time. It was as a result of the recent high level of interest and orders received from Wales and the bordering English counties.

In July of the same year the *West Briton* reporter, Barrie Bennetts, wrote that the Tomahawk big bale shredder had won the Royal Agricultural Society of England's silver medal. According to Barrie, the machine "bore Teagle's hallmarks of simple engineering and good build and finish...providing substantial time and labour savings".

In Pursuit of Excellence was a book which set out to show that Cornwall was not just cream teas, beaches and holidays. It was the brainchild of Michael Galsworthy, the High Sheriff of Cornwall. Published in 1994, it featured 62 companies of excellence – many were major exporters. The directors and staff of Teagle Machinery Ltd were delighted to be included. In its distinctive yellow livery the booklet was widely circulated and sent out the clear message that Cornwall meant business.

In an article for *Farmers' Weekly* Fred Teagle attributed the company's success to its agricultural roots and its continued close contact with farmers. He reflected that it was easy to dwell on the disadvantages it faced of being situated in Cornwall with high transportation costs for both the delivery of steel and for conveying the finished products to the customer but, despite that, business was booming.

John Teagle reflected that until 1985 Teagles had no sales department. It had become apparent that no modern-day company could compete without one and John moved from design to become the company's first Sales Director. He said, "Prior to that we took turns to visit dealers and the nearest thing that we had to a salesman was Tommy James, the demonstrator/lorry driver". John led the entire sales team for about 10 years until, on the 1st February 1995, Geoff Osborne was welcomed on to the

Board as the Director for Home Market Sales – the first non-family member to be made a director. Geoff said, "It was a move sideways to Sales and Marketing but a move upwards onto the Board".

At that time, there were just three area managers: Chris White in Banbury covering the South-East and South Wales, Peter Hagan in Stafford covering the whole of the UK north of Stafford – North Wales, Northern England and Scotland – and the South-West managed by Sharon Elliott, a farmer's daughter from Gorran. To ease the load on the two "upcountry" managers a demonstrator, Graham Cooper, also spent some time in each patch. Geoff said, "He was a good lad, was well liked and I felt that he would do well as a Sales Manager so we created a new area for him. To do this we split Wales from the other two guys, leaving them with smaller territories but still big by today's standards. We then appointed a new demonstrator, Mike Sanders, for the South-East and North but, soon after, he was promoted to South-West area manager when Sharon left to start a family. After a while, I felt that the sales force would run better if the South-East and Northern territories were split into three, with the demonstrator becoming an area manager and each being responsible for everything which went on in their patch, including demonstrations. Additional area managers, Gary Eastham, Steve Offland and David Threadgold, were appointed, which gave us five territories. There were various minor changes along the way but probably the last big milestone was when we decided that we would do better in Scotland if we had someone operating up there – someone who spoke the lingo. We now have a Scotsman, David Haggart, covering Scotland and the biggest problem we have is in understanding him when he's in full flow!"

The six-territory arrangement works well. There was less travelling for everyone and the reduction in size meant that no one was away from home for more than one or two nights a week. The patches were big enough to be worthwhile but small enough for them to do a really good job and, of major importance, to keep close contact with their dealers. Geoff said, "They all worked well together and helped each other with shows and major demonstrations".

This arrangement in the sales team provided John Teagle with time to focus on the challenge of seeking a distributor for each country with a potential market and developing a working relationship, often in a culture quite different from our own. This required John to spend time with potential clients and demanded a substantial proportion of his time in travelling both within Europe and further afield.

More recently the challenge has been to maintain a steady demand against a volatile backdrop in Eastern Europe.

John Teagle has some interesting stories about his experience of working in foreign markets. It is a role which he clearly enjoys. as this account indicates. "I originally became involved in visiting customers and demonstrating in the 1970s and was soon trying to keep in touch with all of our customers world-wide. It was an exhausting time covering an area now shared by 11 people. Once we began employing salesmen the benefits of knocking on doors became more obvious and when Geoff Osborne took over the UK market it left me with more time to concentrate on export. Most of my time and effort was in developing sales of the Tomahawk bale shredders in Europe. Initially, I travelled the continent with a car trailer taking the machines to new customers and putting them to work. Until the UK became part of the EU it meant losing at least half a day at Le Havre, waiting for the correct paperwork to clear customs, a process which seems archaic nowadays.

1996 – Sharon Elliott demonstrating the Superted

There were some adventurous experiences such as taking the car trailer over the Alps in a blizzard and there were also frustrating times like when my engine failed in Germany. Sometimes I hired a car and have always been surprised how easy it is to drive away with no knowledge of local driving laws. For instance, in some countries it is acceptable to ignore a red light to merge with traffic going in the same direction whilst in others it is strictly forbidden. My practice is to take things cautiously rather than make assumptions – it is better to be hooted at than fined! Speed limits are regularly displayed but rarely do they tell you what they are when pulling a trailer. In Germany once, with an empty trailer, I was driving along a motorway going at a speed comparatively slowly compared to the large number of cars towing trailers. A police car came up behind me but because I was driving reasonably slowly I continued at the same speed. Suddenly, there were flashing lights and at the next rest area I found, to my cost, that the speed limit was rather slower! In Switzerland I was stopped and told that I could drive no further because the load I was carrying was wider than the trailer: something which is illegal under Swiss law. This seemed to be an insurmountable problem until I found a length of timber which was longer than the width of the machine. I nailed it to the trailer making it wider than the machine. Amazingly, this was accepted and I was able to continue with my journey.

The most memorable times have been flights to long-haul destinations. On a couple of these it meant a very early-morning start. On one return journey, in Tokyo, I planned to travel to the airport late in the evening. This was to avoid an expensive night in the city and a confusing early-morning train journey with its associated risks of arriving at the wrong destination. However, on the way to the airport the train stopped and everyone had to get out. No English was being spoken and I assumed that it was the time of night when trains stopped, even though they had not reached their scheduled destinations. I took a taxi for the remainder of the journey and on arrival at the airport I looked around for somewhere to sleep. It was summer so I settled on an outdoor bench. I was almost asleep when a policeman approached me and told me to get up. I feared that I was being arrested for vagrancy but instead I was shepherded to a terminal building where there was an area where there were other overnight visitors. They were trying to sleep on benches which had been designed to prevent people doing just that. I proceeded to open my suitcase, take out my sleeping bag and, with a distinct air of superiority, settle down to sleep on the floor. Now, whenever I see a 'Mr Bean' film, I imagine how I must have looked.

I found Japan to have a very quirky culture. I once saw a man coming out of a smoking cubicle and immediately putting on a mask, as if the atmosphere outside the cubicle was worse than inside it. Clothes worn as daily wear by teenagers can seem very strange, with girls wearing a tutus or pink frilly creations as if going to a fancy-dress party. On one occasion I was introduced to someone who did not speak English and, as we shook hands, he said something that I did not understand. My translator explained that he had said that I was very handsome. He looked quite 'straight' but that was the end of that conversation.

My first visit to Belarus was to visit a customer who was to become quite important to us. I was collected from the airport by a technician in a company van. It was January and cold – an especially cold period. We were travelling back to their office when the van stopped. The extreme cold had frozen the petrol. To make matters worse the heating failed and we had to wait in the cold for another car to save us. Mobile phones can sometimes be very useful!

On the way to the USA I once visited Iceland, where the only road which was being kept clear of snow was from the airport to the capital, Reykjavik. On other roads layer on layer of snow builds up but people get used to it and simply carry on as best they can. The drama we experience when a few flakes of snow fall in this country seems totally unreasonable. During that visit our importer took me to an outdoor swimming pool which was supplied by hot water from underground springs. It was a surrealistic experience to be in a hot swimming pool and yet be able to reach out for some snow and make a snowball.

I once visited Colombia when it was in the news rather more than it is now. I had to visit an importer who had just received a Tomahawk. I wanted to establish if we could do more business. I was warned that when walking around the capital, Bogotá, I should not accept anything from anyone. Even accepting a glass of water could well result in waking up having been robbed or being held as a hostage. We had to fly to the other side of a mountain range to see a farmer – the same mountain range where terrorists lived. However, I spoke to many Colombians and left with a feeling that they could well be the friendliest people in the world. It was a similar story in Northern Ireland during their 'troubles' where the people I met were as easy-going and friendly as you could ever hope to find."

Fred recalls that in the late 1960s when he was looking for alternative suppliers of axles for the Titan trailers, he and Dinah went on a visit to Poland on the chance that he could work up some reciprocal business in the country. Having obtained the required visas (written totally in Polish) they eventually arrived in Communist Warsaw. They booked into their very basic hotel accommodation and not having visited a Communist country before, always had that strange feeling of being watched. The next morning they arrived at the address, a very austere office block. After a good half an hour's wait in a cold

foyer, they were ushered into a room on the fifth floor that was obviously being hurriedly emptied of typists. The sales manager was sitting behind his desk in the corner of the eventually cleared room. The meeting commenced. It did not go well – the manager had no specifications nor any prices for the axles he was supposed to be selling, and to add to the confusion, did not have an agricultural machinery background, so there was very little chance of them taking any Teagle kit.

With no improvement, the following day in the city, they crossed a virtually deserted dual carriageway, only to hear whistles blowing from all directions. Within seconds four policemen apprehended them and fined them on the spot for jaywalking. The departure at the airport was no better. Dinah was processed through emigration – no problem. Fred, on the other hand, was taken aside into a separate room and it was explained to him that his visa had expired on the previous day (so much for understanding Polish!). He had to pay a hefty fine in sterling before he was eventually allowed to join Dinah aboard the aircraft. We think Dinah may have been glad to see him! – so much for the pleasures of foreign business trips. The company purchased some sample axles, but found the business environment too problematic to continue trading with Poland.

Now, with the use of the internet, more people can access information on our products and we are increasingly getting more enquiries from countries where we have never done business. I have always been overwhelmed by the hospitality extended to me by customers and by the local people of those countries who just want me to enjoy being there. It has been a great experience turning disinterested customers into enthusiastic ones and experiencing the different cultures of other countries. There are still many countries where we could be selling so there is still much work to do as well as continuing to develop our existing markets."

We have already mentioned that the UK was divided into six areas, but worldwide, the system adopted was somewhat different. Each country typically had one agent or main distributor who either sold direct or through a network of sub-distributors.

With a greater focus on export it became clear that extra emphasis was required on aftermarket service. In addition the need for a high level of quality was more important than ever, with machines required to work in more extreme conditions and work reliably in remote locations.

It also became clear that specific engineering solutions would be required, tailored to local farming practices, tractors and machinery. To this end Duncan Wilson, Teagles Engineering Director, and his Service Manager travel to meet distributors, dealers and machine operators.

Ingenuity is a word that could have been invented to describe Tom Teagle. It was Tom's ingenuity that gave birth to the business and it was his ingenuity that had kept it at the forefront of the agricultural manufacturing world. New ideas and the continual development of proven technology had moulded this little country business into one that had become established as a world leader. In the 1990s it was the *West Briton and Royal Cornwall Gazette* which used the word in an article as it trumpeted that it was "Ingenuity that took the drudgery out of work". John Jasper was reviewing a new book from Farming Press entitled *Fifty Years of Garden Machinery*. In it he referred to the part played by Teagle Machinery at the smaller end of the market. The machinery produced at

1996 – Work-placement student Andrew Stone in the drawing office with not a drawing board in sight

Blackwater had become so sophisticated and so important to the large farms that it was easy to ignore the part played in satisfying the needs of the market gardeners and smallholders over the years. The book, by Brian Bell, was intended for machinery enthusiasts and collectors and included a range of Teagle machines such as the grass-trimmers, hedge-trimmers, lawn mowers, sprayers and cultivators.

When Geoff Osborne moved to head the home sales team, Duncan Wilson took over as manager of the design department. In 2003 he was promoted to the Board as engineering director responsible for the design and development of new products and for their quality control. The role involved receiving ideas and determining whether or not the prospect was viable or likely to fail by reason of cost or performance. If it was decided that the project would "fly," then the necessary information was produced to enable it to proceed to the production shop floor. Duncan said, "Even after nearly 30 years in the manufacturing sector I still get a buzz from seeing one of our machines working in a field, producing foodstuff for the nation".

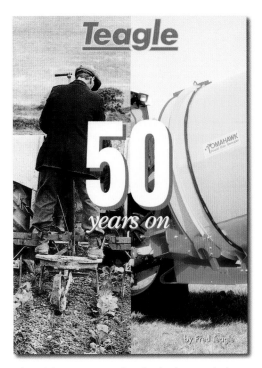

The 50th anniversary book which provided some much-needed funds for St Julia's Hospice

Presentation of the cheque to St Julia's Hospice

In 1993, Teagles celebrated its 50th anniversary and three years later a book was produced to commemorate the milestone. The date, of course, relates to incorporation and not to the commencement of manufacture which began about six years before, in 1937. Fred Teagle devoted considerable time to produce this colourful publication which tells the history of the company and displays many of its machines which had been designed and produced over the years. The trademark colours of bright red and yellow made it look very attractive and profits from sales were directed towards a very worthy cause, St Julia's Hospice. Fred stated then, and it is still true today, that the company's fortunes were at the whims of politicians both at home and in Europe and that to be able to read any consistent policy into their dealings needs something more than a crystal ball.

Come and buy our brightly coloured machines! A staged photograph for the 50-year anniversary book.

The January/February 1997 edition of *Contract and Crops* posed a question. In actual fact it was more of a statement, but it asked what Tom Teagle's vision had been for the future of his company. Did he, in those very early days, see it as an add-on to his farm or did he believe that it would grow into an organisation that would eclipse and eventually replace the farming activity at Tywarnhayle — one that would spread its trading tentacles right across the world? Without doubt he was blessed with an inventive flair and a confidence to match but to succeed he was going to have to compete with the best, many of which employed qualified engineers with years of experience. It would take an exceptional and remarkable man to win through against such competition but with our benefit of hindsight it is clear to see that he was just that. The early potato planter, the steerage hoe, the tipping carts and the thousands of fertilizer spreaders

all played their part but it was one man's drive and tenacity at the right time which laid the foundation for the future.

The success of *In Pursuit of Excellence* prompted the Cornwall Exporter of the Year Awards in 1997 and the issue of another publication. Once again, it featured Teagles with a photograph of a bale shredder and the comment, "Exports of bale shredders and other forms of farm machinery by Teagle Machinery of Blackwater have doubled over the last twelve months and helped the company to become a world market leader". The award ceremony was sponsored by Barclays. It was held at the Goldsmiths' Hall in London and Mary Teagle was there to meet the Duke of Kent.

The summer of 1997 saw the installation of the first Edwards Pearson CNC hydraulic press brake. Complicated shapes had

1998 – Mary Teagle, wife of the founder, with the Duke of Kent, vice-chairman of the British Overseas Trade Board

1999 – Royal Cornwall Show with a smiling Geoff Osborne (now minus the beard) – no doubt the flowers were a present for his wife, Jenny

previously been made from flat sections and angles bolted together, or by older-fashioned folding machines, but this new piece of equipment, once programmed, could bend components to the required shape and to a degree of accuracy never before achieved by the company. The potential of these machines did not go unnoticed by the workforce. Perhaps a few perceived them as a threat to their jobs but that was not the intention, nor was it how events turned out. Indeed, the employees were encouraged to play a part in choosing which machinery best suited the company's

1999 – Geoff Osborne again, this time with an award at the Royal Highland Show

needs. With a three-metre bed and a bending force of 100 tonnes the new aquisition greatly increased the company's ability to compete in the marketplace and the spring 1998 edition of Landwards stated that Teagles were producing about 2,700 machines in a typical year. Using conventional folding machines, changing operations was a long-winded process and it was only cost-effective to produce components in long runs. That meant tying up a considerable amount of capital and occupying precious floor space. The switch to CNC press brakes, where the programmed information was retained in the memory and used to call up repeat batches, meant that changing operations was greatly simplified, allowing small batches to be produced – say a week's requirement of 25 or 30 at a time – and still keeping the unit cost down. A second machine was added in 1998. It had a wider, four-metre, bed and a bending force of 150 tonnes. Such machines represented a considerable capital expenditure but the saving in production cost was considerable and in 2008, when the first machine was approaching the end of its life, the directors had no hesitation in replacing it with a four-metre Bystronic press brake. This machine could be programmed to make up to 32 bends on one component and represented a further improvement to the process. In 2014, three press brakes were working continuously and the demand is such that the installation of a fourth could be justified.

Looking back, Geoff Osborne reflected on the way that customer expectations had driven up standards. He said, "After the Second World War the country, and the agricultural industry, was in a state of recovery. As long as you produced something that worked then people would beat a path to your door. Teagles had a reputation for producing machines which worked well but were a bit cheap and cheerful. They were certainly innovative, however, and there was a well-used expression that if there was a strong enough spring, a long enough belt and enough wire rope then Tom Teagle would have been the first man on the moon."

"Tough times for farmers," was the newspaper headline in May 1998 and this was reflected in the drop in cattle entries at the Royal Cornwall Show. Of course, if farmers were feeling the pinch then the suppliers to that industry would very soon see the effect in terms of reduced sales. One well-known machinery supplier experienced a drop of almost 50% and it is difficult to imagine many businesses surviving such a massive reduction in revenue. Teagles were not immune to this downturn but in their case it was more like a 25% reduction as they were still experiencing reasonable trading levels with the USA and the Scandinavian countries. Undoubtedly the company's emphasis on new inventions and continued innovation played a large part in their ability to survive the financial storm.

The Royal Cornwall Show is always a pleasure to attend if only for the annual ritual of meeting familiar faces on the stands and amongst the thousands of loyal supporters. It is now much more than just an agriculture show but farming is still at its heart. It is a Mecca for the Cornish farming community and one of the majors for many exhibitors. For Teagles too, it is a must and as Geoff Osborne said, "You have to be at all the big agricultural shows to keep your name at the forefront of the market place but the Royal Cornwall is a bit special. It's very difficult to put a value on being there but it's all part of gaining customer feedback and any resultant sales can often be months later. It is also a good chance to see what everyone else is doing!"

Tucked away in the archives are numerous letters from people who have managed to find and refurbish some elderly pieces of Teagle farm machinery. Many items have received a great deal of loving care and attention and now take their place in the historical displays at annual shows. One such letter came from Jonathan Hockedy who had restored a Teagle two-stroke engine which, he understood, had been owned by Raymond Baxter, the WW2 pilot and television personality. Another such letter arrived in the in-tray and asked for piston rings for two 1960 four-stroke engines. Yet another came from Paul Adams who had found a Teagle Cyclemotor which was to be put on display in his Runcorn Cycle and Cyclemotor Museum. In 2010 David Williams of Cheltenham wrote to say that he had acquired a fertilizer spinner/spreader. He asked the year of manufacture and colour so that he could return it to its original appearance.

1999 – Teagle machines can be found in many far-flung and exotic places but from the amount of interest shown here we can imagine that there are not too many in Costa Rica – full marks for the improvised roof to the tractor cab

2000s

The dreaded foot-and-mouth outbreak in 2001 was critical for the country, agriculture and for the companies which served that industry. Teagle Machinery was no different. For most of us it meant regular bulletins of dreadful news and harrowing pictures of funeral pyres but for Teagles it had a worrying impact on the bottom line. It left them with no choice but to introduce staff lay-offs. Fortunately, the export market continued but with enquiries and orders from within the UK decimated, about 25% of the staff were made redundant. The farming community was reduced to fire-fighting mode and in no position to place orders for new machinery. It was a difficult time for both the company and its employees and there was a genuine hope that many could be re-employed as soon as there was some sign of recovery. The installation of a fourth Farley plasma cutter around this time signalled hope for the future.

Like most successful companies, Teagles history has been one of constant change and improvement but if we were looking to identify a period when this was most pronounced then perhaps we should look at what has become known as the noughties. Certainly, the advances in production accelerated during this decade and the quality of product showed great improvement. This does not imply inactivity during the previous years, far from it, as without the necessary foundations there can be no structure, but this period does seem to be when Teagles really came of age and became recognised as a world-class company.

Production manager John Veall retired in 2003. During his 50 years with the company he worked in the machine shop, the welding area, was a workshop foreman at the age of 23, foreman of the assembly area and was promoted to the position of works manager. John considered himself very lucky to have had such a long and happy career with a company which provided so many families with a good living. John's successor was Jon Cox who had previously worked for the engineering company J & F Pool of Hayle. The timing of his succession allowed for a four-month overlap with John Veall, something, he felt, to be

Receiving the award at the 2000 Royal Show is Duncan Wilson and shaking hands with Fred Teagle is Nick Brown from the Ministry of Agriculture, Fisheries and Food (MAFF)

John Veall shortly before he retired

in strategy for both production and for the company as a whole.

By 2006 the Tuckingmill site had stood empty, or virtually empty, for over 20 years. At last, however, there was the prospect of a sale. The premises, which had been the scene of great change during its life would soon be put to a different use. A part was allocated for housing and the remainder was to be a commercial development. The conclusion of the sale also brought to a close an important chapter in the life of the company. Thge site had been where Teagles had grown and diversified into the manufacture of new and larger products but it had also had seen their withdrawal to centralise their activities at Blackwater. The proceeds of the sale enabled the company to clear its debts and to make substantial investments in plant and machinery – it gave the directors the confidence to build for the future.

invaluable. He said, "It helped me adapt to the Teagle way of getting things done. It was a completely different philosophy here with a big emphasis on giving the customer what he wanted. If that meant adapting a product to suit a particular need then that was what we did. As a consequence, there was a certain amount of work which could not be planned." Two years later, in 2005, Jon was offered the position of production director. He was still in charge of all shop floor activities but he was also a member of the Board with an involvement

Royal Smithfield Show in 2002

Mary Teagle had been a major part of the business from its early stages. Her contribution had reduced in recent years but she was still on hand and still very interested in its activities. Some have referred to her as a great organiser with a brain like a computer and perhaps that was essential considering Tom's propensity for design rather than administration. Her death, on the 2nd January 2008, marked the end of an era. Those present at her funeral heard how she had been held in the highest regard by all who had dealings with the company. They heard, too, that she had acquired a reputation for being a tad formidable in her business life. She often answered incoming calls and most agreed that her telephone manner was rather abrupt and not always conducive to fostering warm relationships. In fact, when agents needed to discuss a warranty problem they would draw straws to determine who would make the call. However, she did have a much softer side. Her involvement with her family was

The October 2006 issue of Profi included a delightful photograph of Mary Teagle with her 20-month old great-grandson, Samuel (Roger's son), browsing a back copy of the same magazine. It said that 92-year-old Mary kept a close and vastly experienced eye on his bedtime reading material and suggested that the future of Teagle Machinery seemed to be in good hands.

very different and her grandchildren and great-grandchildren have good reason to remember her for the warmth and affection she showed towards them.

Roger Teagle, Fred's son, has his own IT consultancy in Cheltenham but he is also one of the third-generation directors at Teagles. He attended Brunel University where he studied Manufacturing Engineering. Following a period working for Westland Helicopters he moved to a software company before starting its own business. His extensive knowledge of the use of software on the shop floor makes him an invaluable member of the team. Fred's younger son, Colin, is the Project Development Manager. After gaining his degree from Loughborough University he spent some time with Rolls-Royce and Jaguar before running his own public house. His current role at Teagles includes the purchase of new equipment and buildings and the design of the shop floor layouts to ensure a smooth flow of components along the production line.

By 2010, Geoff Osborne had been the director for home market sales for about 15 years and, with retirement looming, it was time to consider passing the reins to someone a bit younger. That person was Tom Teagle, one of the founder's grandsons. Tom Teagle Jnr joined the company in June 2007 after studying Mechanical Engineering, also at Brunel University, and subsequently working in industry; a year at Rolls-Royce in naval engineering, six years with German engineering company Mannesmann in Automated Logisitics, and a further few years working in construction project management with the Australian supermarket Coles Myer. Following his return to Cornwall he was delighted to be invited to become a part of the company which his grandfather had created. "It was a little daunting," he said. "Joining the family firm is not always straightforward but for me, it has been a rewarding experience. The members of the family and the other directors have all been very supportive."

At first, Tom was involved in the spares department but before long he moved to sales where he worked alongside his father, John, and Geoff Osborne. He became the UK sales manager and, when Geoff stood down, he took over his role. Geoff retained his position on the Board and, having relinquished his sales function, he was able to devote his time to special projects in the marketing department. It was an expanding area which had not been given too high a priority in the past.

Succession planning is often ignored in companies but, with an eye to the future, Tom's responsibility was extended to include Europe, building on the work undertaken by his father in this region. This left John with time to concentrate on Eastern Europe and the little matter of the rest of the world. The latter, of course, included the very important and potentially huge market in the United States of America.

With Roger, Colin, Tom and Robin in the company, four of the founder's eight grandchildren are there to ensure the continuation of the name.

Life changed for Fred Teagle in 2005 – to some extent. Since his father died he had held the reins as managing director and his input by way of time and energy was considerable. Full retirement, however, was not an option. Yes, he wanted to reduce his day-to-day involvement but he had no wish to stand down completely. The answer was to make him company chairman. This gave him the time to pursue his other interests whilst retaining his involvement with the company. It was a solution which suited everyone.

A further restructuring included three other appointments: Jim Squires became UK sales manager and Werner Brach took over as sales manager for Europe. In addition Andy Robson was taken on as sales manager for North America, based in North Carolina.

For a company that had previously shunned the need for any sales and marketing activity Teagles had made a substantial commitment to this very necessary function. Tom Teagle, in his role as sales director, was delighted to reflect on the stability within the team, which had an average of 10 years employment with the company.

Agricultural shows continued to provide a good opportunity for contact with customers, both existing and potential, and the company regularly exhibited with its own stand at 15 events in the United Kingdom. Additionally, its products were displayed at exhibitions around the globe – from France to North America Teagles exhibit in their own right. Whether standing in a wet field, or among the razzmatazz at the Hannover Messe for Agritechnica the Teagle Sales team will be found, usually with a warm drink and some Cornish saffron cake and fairings to offer.

As communication and shipping around the globe become easier and less expensive the competition that Teagle face, whether in the UK or in export markets, grows ever greater. With manufacturers vying for the attention of farmers and distrbutors in every market, the effort that is required from the Sales and Marketing team increases. It is not only necessary to visit markets to understand their specific requirements, guide and encourage distributors, but also to work on developing Teagles' corporate image.

Whilst advertising and production of sales materials such as brochures had largely been left to Teagles distributors in the past, it was now necessary to take control of production of advertisements, brochures, exhibitions and increasingly importantly, the website.

The importance of making the farmers feel comfortable with what they are being offered cannot be overstated. Teagle invest heavily to ensure that products are well presented, with materials from sales leaflets to instruction books published in the local language.

As we have said, marketing in its wider sense was a relatively new activity for the company but the emphasis placed on it during the noughties was an indication of the importance it had then acquired. Underlining this was the appointment of a marketing manager in November 2012 which further strengthened the team.

Spare parts also came under the broad heading of Sales and Marketing. Being a part of Sales, the newest team in the company, it is perhaps ironic that the spare parts department is located in one of the oldest buildings – one of the few remaining buildings from the farming

The spares stores, the last remaining original farm building left in 2015

days and the place where the cows stood at the stalls as they were milked.

When Teagles bought W & W A Heyden Machinery in 1977, general manager, Fred Harris, was placed in charge of the Plain-an-Gwarry workshop. Eventually, when they relocated to the Blackwater site in 1990, Fred also moved, and in August 2007, after an amazing 75 years in the industry, he decided at the age of 90 that he wanted to cut back a bit on his working week. Barrie Bennetts of the *West Briton* was on hand to produce an article about

him. He wrote that Fred had joined Heyden Engineering as an apprentice and had spent all his working life there. As retirement age loomed he had felt that he was not ready to put his feet up and when the workforce relocated to Blackwater he continued to work about 24 hours a week, repairing and setting machine tools and doing specialised jobs.

Over the years Shop 7 saw a huge investment in computer-controlled lathes and machining centres, which in turn provided the company with a 'state

2009 – Two of the five CNC lathes in Shop 7 – the precision machine shop

of the art' precision machine shop which was able to supply all the high quality machined parts needed for its products.

Research and development is as important in this type of business as in any other and to remain at the forefront in a competitive market it is essential to be able to sell the benefits of a product. Whether that relates to being able to use a forage wagon as an ordinary trailer or using research data on the optimum length of shredded straw, it is an excellent way to promote a company's goods.

Perhaps, even from those early days, that was exactly what Tom Teagle was doing. Maybe that was the reason for his success and why the name of Teagle is still at the forefront of agricultural development. It cannot be undertaken without considerable cost, however, and it currently involves approximately 10% of the workforce.

The old Shop 6 (once a Dutch barn) had been erected in the late 1950s. It was

The Edwards Pearson PR 150 Bystronic CNC hydraulic press brakes

2014 – The latest Machining Centre

where the concrete mixer drums were made. In November 2008 it was time for it to go and by May the following year it had been replaced by a brand-new building. The new building was considerably larger and the additional space meant that much of the cutting operation previously carried out in Shop 3 could be transferred there. The knock-on benefit meant that the vacated floor-space in Shop 3 could be put to use as additional welding bays.

By 2009 there was a need for a larger

2009 – The Centerliner

and more sophisticated fertilizer distributor but the development team was busy concentrating on designing feeder-bedders and had little time to spend on building and testing such an involved machine. The answer was the introduction of the range of equipment produced by Peeters Landbouwmachines. Their cultivation and drilling machinery, together with their renowned Centerliner fertilizer distributor, proved to be a great success.

2010 - The Vario cultivator

The 2009 stand at the SIMA exhibition in Paris

2009 Royal Highland Show

2010s

Yet another of the old farm buildings was standing in the way of progress. The binder house had ended its first life in the 1950s and, since then, it had been used to test engines and for storage. Now, in February 2010, it was time for it to make way for future developments.

Just a few months later, Shop 5 was re-clad, bringing the insulation factor up to modern standards. May 2010 saw the removal of yet more old buildings and the erection of a structure interestingly referred to as the "Tent". This somewhat more temporary building provided a much-needed undercover storage space. Later that year, in August, the car park was extended to provide room for an additional 30 cars, and an Elliott-type building was erected to provide canteen facilities for those who wished to use them. Perhaps strangely, many chose to continue to remain near their workplace where they would settle down for bite to eat and a game of lunchtime euchre.

September 2012 saw the installation of a Davi CNC four-roll machine. This fascinating piece of equipment rolls sheet metal into curves like the cylinders for the bale shredders and the drums for the concrete mixers. The original three-roller version necessitated part of the process being undertaken by the press brakes but the new machine was able to carry out the complete job.

If we reflect on the early days, the products that flowed out of the factory gates were nowhere near as colourful as they are now. Denzil Moyle recalled that one early choice was blue and aluminium. Now, however, the products are immediately identified by being bright red and yellow. The colours seem to portray an industry which is less drab than some would have us believe. Perhaps they are meant to remind us of our childhood toys, in which case the choice could be said to be ingenious and probably made by some marketing guru for some psychological reason. The idea of combining red with yellow, however, seems to have come from across the water. The Tipmix was popular in Ireland but John Teagle recalled an importer who considered that sales would improve if, instead of it being entirely red, the drum was painted yellow. Whether this was a Celtic connection with bright colours, or simply because he liked the combination, we do not know, but it worked, and from then on those colours have been used.

There was one exception, however, when one model of the elevator was finished in aluminium. This was done to give the impression of a machine which was both lightweight and easily transportable. It turned out to be an unpopular choice. When it reappeared the following year it was painted in the customary colours. Ironically, one disparaging comment received had been that the aluminium colour made it appear to be too light and flimsy!

For some years there had been a realisation that the appearance of the finished product was not as good as it could or should be. Functionality was of paramount importance but, as when buying a car, the decision about which one to choose was often based on appearance. Customer expectations had increased and with tractors becoming more sophisticated and matching the quality of finish on a car, it was reasonable to conclude that the accessories had to keep pace. The quality of finish could no longer be ignored.

An improvement was, of course, achieveable but the higher standard would mean yet another large capital outlay. Up until this time, components had been dipped or sprayed under basic conditions. The paint never fully hardened and a considerable amount of time was wasted repairing paint damage. Stacked components often stuck together and paint was chipped when the machines were roped down on the lorry. A powder-coating system was the way forward. This was a process in which coloured powder was applied electrostatically and then cured at 180 degrees centigrade (hot enough to cook a pasty!) to allow it to flow and form a finish that was much harder than conventional paint. From February to August 2010, Shop 3 was extended and a shot-blasting plant and powder-coating line installed. It was a major step forward in improving the quality of the product. Added to that was the benefit that it became possible to manufacture, paint and fit a part all in one day. It also overcame environmental problems related to spray-painting as there were no harmful solvents in the atmosphere. Any surplus powder falling to the floor was simply recycled.

These installations dealt with most of the products but the larger items, the trailers and dung-spreaders, were simply too big for the powder-coating line and, for a while, these were painted by an outside company. In 2013, however, two large booths were incorporated into the newly-constructed Shop 4B. One was a shot-blasting chamber and the other a state of the art spray-booth.

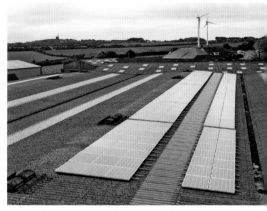

The solar panels, with turbines in the distance

In February 2012, in an effort to increase the company's green credentials, a 50kw wind turbine was installed in an adjacent field. The following month, a 100kw solar panel roof installation was erected on Shop 3, and when Shop 4B was finished a further 50kw installation was installed on its roof. After that, if the sun shone and the wind blew, the total potential generation was about one third of the company's needs. Realistically, the generation of something approaching 25% of the total requirements was deemed a success.

2012 – Livestock Event

Press day for the launch of the updated Tomahawks at Moreton Morrell College, Warwickshire, in 2012

2013 Cereals Event

C. 1949 – Tom Teagle on his MM tractor with a young Fred to the right and one of his workmen

The entrance to the site has changed considerably over the years. Initially it served the farm, and this photograph of Tom Teagle driving through the traditional granite gate-posts is in complete contrast to the wide access road which now serves the factory. In August 2012, new entrance signage and flagpoles were erected, which must have caused a few passing locals to wonder what went on in this factory.

On a visit to Cornwall in March 2012, Peter Kendall, the NFU President, met a group of local farmers at the Blackwater factory. He was not short on criticism of government policies but reserved as the main target for his wrath their predecessors and, in particular, the policies of Margaret Beckett.

In the same month, George Eustice, the MP for Camborne and Redruth, referred to his visit to the factory of this company which he considered to be "A great Cornish success story". He called for more support for such manufacturing companies which were world leaders in their chosen field who brought much-

An up-to-date photograph of the drive

The entrance signage and flagpoles

David and Fred Teagle with George Eustice, Member of Parliament for Camborne and Redruth (centre) – during his visit in March 2012

needed exports to our shores. Of course, Britain still has a sizeable manufacturing base but it shrank considerably during the 1980s and his appeal for more support was in stark contrast to the non-interventionist polices of that era.

The company is now heavily reliant on IT, which has made it possible to achieve a level of manufacturing excellence that previous generations of businessmen could not even imagine. Through its use, the company is better able to compete in an increasingly competitive world and better equipped to consider the "what if" scenario – what if we do it this way or what if we redesign this part? Most notable are the aspects directly related to production, the computer-linked machines or the pieces of equipment with their own "brains". There are now many aspects of business life in which software can be used to make life easier and improve the bottom line.

A prestigious gold medal award at the Royal Cornwall Show in 2012 was a fitting reward for the company's display of new machinery. Tom Teagle Jnr referred to the annual event as an outstanding show which reflected the

level of support received from the local farming community. There is no doubt that the Royal Cornwall Show is a credit to Cornwall. Its huge appeal has seen it improve and grow from its previous nomadic nature when it was held in various sites across the Duchy. It is now centred on Wadebridge where it has a permanent site and is well served with the necessary infrastructure and services.

When Mary Teagle died, the farmhouse ceased to be used as a dwelling. For the family, the building held many personal memories both as a family home where Tom and Mary raised their sons and as a base for the administrative and sales aspects for the growing company. It was destined to have a new purpose. By December 2012 it had been renovated and converted into a business centre with excellent meeting and conference facilities.

The increased emphasis on Health and Safety has improved the working environment in the workshops and some of the practices – and the pranks – are now just distant memories. Over the years there have been some near-disasters. Some appear in this book, but whether by luck or good planning there has never been a major incident on the premises. Of course, the moggie which fell into the paint tank would disagree with this!

A three-page spread in the April 2003 edition of *Torque* talked of 88-year-old Mary Teagle "still opening the post". If, however, that made Teagles sound like a dyed-in-the-wool company, hidebound by tradition, then nothing could be further from the truth. Its design team had an average age of less than 25 and the company was using every ounce of modern technology available. The article added that Teagles was one of the most efficient manufacturing outfits in the agricultural manufacturing sector. More importantly, it had flourished and grown when dozens of fellow British manufacturers had closed

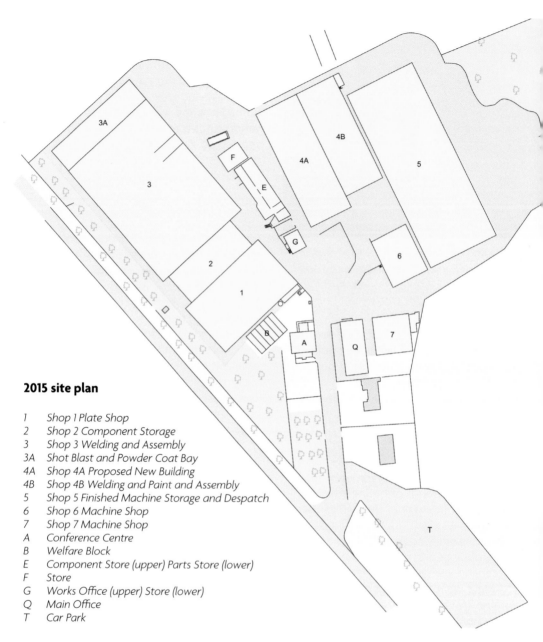

2015 site plan

1	Shop 1 Plate Shop
2	Shop 2 Component Storage
3	Shop 3 Welding and Assembly
3A	Shot Blast and Powder Coat Bay
4A	Shop 4A Proposed New Building
4B	Shop 4B Welding and Paint and Assembly
5	Shop 5 Finished Machine Storage and Despatch
6	Shop 6 Machine Shop
7	Shop 7 Machine Shop
A	Conference Centre
B	Welfare Block
E	Component Store (upper) Parts Store (lower)
F	Store
G	Works Office (upper) Store (lower)
Q	Main Office
T	Car Park

their doors. The article continued by saying that the traditional Cornish work base had been eroded. Fishing and farming were much reduced from their former level and there was scarcely anything left of the mining industry. Teagle Machinery, however, was still there, doing what it does best, and reshaping itself according to the needs of an ever-changing agricultural market.

One obvious disadvantage for the company was in having a factory located so far from its client base. The arterial roads had improved but more dualling was necessary and there was nothing that could be done about the distance. Exeter, traditionally seen as the heart of the West Country, was 90 miles away and Gloucester 200 miles. Despite these drawbacks, however, Blackwater was where the company was conceived and Blackwater is where it will remain. It is a Cornish

*1945 to 2015
developments*

company employing
a substantially local
workforce. It has a
first-hand feel for what
the industry needs and, of
paramount importance, an
understanding of when it is time to
let go of a product and move on to the
next. This then, is a company which is fast
on its feet: developing, modifying and
producing machines with the speed of a
small company but with the expertise of a
world-leader.

■ *1945 production area*
□ *2015 production area*

It was appropriate that such a highly
innovative and very Cornish company
should be involved in the Trevithick engine
replica project. Teagles were delighted
to donate materials and expertise to this
evocative venture. The work culminated

in the re-enactment of Richard Trevithick's
1801 Camborne Hill run made famous
by the song "Going up Camborne Hill".
Kingsley Rickard of the Trevithick Society
presented Fred Teagle with a framed

September 2014 aerial view

Cutting the ribbon in 2014 – Fred Teagle, Tom Teagle, David Teagle, Jon Cox, Duncan Wilson, John Teagle, George Osborne, Chancellor and George Eustice (Member of Parliament for Camborne and Redruth and Parliamentary Under-Secretary of State for Natural Environment, Water and Rural Affairs)

commemorative photo which now hangs on the wall in the entrance foyer.

In May 2013 an important project was under way. It began with the arrival of some large excavating machines which trundled across the island, heading for middle yard. The lower half of the area was removed and before long the steel structure for the new Shop 4B was being erected. Soon, the building was enclosed and the concrete floor was hardening. It is here that the larger machines are built: currently Titan spreaders and, possibly, the big Tomahawks in the future. The building included a new shot-blasting bay and the large spray booth mentioned earlier.

In May 2014 George Osborne, the Chancellor of the Exchequer, visited Cornwall. Included in the itinerary was a tour of the Teagle Factory where he formally opened the newly-completed Shop 4B.

Gordon Bennetts worked at Teagles for 37 years, from October 1971 to 2008, and he spent almost all of his time in the welding bays. As he talked to me in the comfort of his front room he reflected on the changes that had taken place while he was there. The progression from stick welding, with a rod of metal, to MIG welding, with a coil of wire, was a change which had certainly speeded up the process. Some of the welding had been automated but he was pleased to say that in spite of that, the skill of the welder was still required.

The automation referred to was the installation of a robot welder – during the summer of 1997. The machine had been produced in the West Country and, despite what some feared, it did not lead to the diminution of manual welding. Company policy had always been to automate where possible and the introduction of a robot welding system was an obvious move. However, rather than replace the traditional welder, it sat happily alongside him.

September 2013 saw the arrival of yet another leading-edge machine, a Cloos welding robot. Technology had improved considerably since the first robot had been put in place and this machine both improved the weld quality and reduced the time taken by about two thirds. The system has two stations. allowing components to be unloaded from one while the second was at work. The earlier machine was still in use welding smaller components, leaving the Cloos to tackle the larger pieces of work. This was brand-new technology. Those using it had to familiarise themselves with its complexities but, once mastered, the machine was soon producing a consistently superior standard of welding at a greater speed. It could work all day with no breaks for a rest or a cup of tea! By the end of 2014 a third robot had been installed to help cope with the extra component flow.

As mentioned before, there seems amongst local people to be very little appreciation of the extent of the company's activities. Visitors continue to be amazed and impressed when they attend one of the charity open days or other events held at the factory from time to time. Teagles has played host

to many such groups and in February 2013 it welcomed some third-year BSc students from Cornwall College. On show was the Global Positioning System (GPS) technology being used for applying fertilizer. It provides the user with a good indication of where fertilizer is required and is one more example of the use of technology that would astound farmers of previous generations. Tom Teagle, the grandson of the founder, referred to the pride in showing visitors around the factory and giving such students a taste of the real day-to-day issues that businesses face.

A somewhat less technical tour took place on the 5th July 2014 when the company welcomed a group of about 40 people from the Summer Festival celebrations of the Cornwall-wide Federation of Old Cornwall Societies. About 270 members had travelled to

The Cloos robot welder in action

Members of the Federation of Old Cornwall Societies touring the factory

2014 – Greenpower Racing Project supporting Richard Lander School in Truro

St Agnes to take part in the annual event. Having agreed to host the Old Cornwall Society group, Teagles decided to combine it with an open day during which they raised almost £800 for the Greenpower Racing Projects at Richard Lander School, Mithian Primary School and Mount Hawke Academy. Many groups were treated to a guided tour and one in particular was probably a world first. Tristan Chubb, a welder at the factory, provided a tour for the Agan Tavas support group during which the commentary was made entirely in Kernewek (The Cornish language).

Teagles is one of the UK's major manufacturers of agricultural machinery and to show its appreciation for its wide client base, and the support it had received from the farming community, Fred Teagle presented a cheque for £1,000 to Pam Wills, Regional Manager of RABI (Royal Agriculture Benevolent Institution), during her visit in the autumn of 2013. Since then, a further £1,000 and two commercial pressure washers have been donated to help the farming community affected by the 2014 Somerset flooding.

As we head towards the conclusion of this book there is yet another development in progress. Additional production space is needed and a new building – Shop 4A – is under construction to meet this need.

Teagle Machinery Ltd is a modern-thinking company making full use of the latest technological and management techniques. The application of more sophisticated planning and marketing over the past 20 years has turned it into a world-class business which firmly believes that the sale of concepts and benefits leads to greater sales of products.

It was back in 1937 that Tom Teagle began manufacturing as a sole trader, and six years later, in 1943, the business was incorporated as W T Teagle (Machinery) Ltd. It would be fascinating to have the sales figures from day one but we do know that by 1949 the turnover was in excess of £40,000. Of course, that was based on the value of the pound at that time and, if we make the adjustment to show the equivalent figure for 2015, we would be talking of a turnover in excess of one million pounds. By the mid-1950s, sales had risen to over a quarter of a million pounds and during the 1960s and 1970s there was continuous growth during which the turnover rose to approximately 2.7 million pounds or about 9 million pounds converted to today's figures. This growth came to an abrupt end in 1980 when there was a large drop in sales, particularly of hedge-trimmers to France. This was reflected in the turnover, which dropped by over a third. The 1980s were not an easy time for the reasons we have discussed earlier and it was a

case of holding on until the national and international financial situation improved. The 1990s started slowly but, within a couple of years, sales began to improve and a pattern of sustained growth was established. It has continued to the present day when the turnover for the current year is expected to be in the region of £14 million.

The company's exporting experience dates back to the 1940s but it was about 20 years later that overseas sales grew to become a sizeable proportion of the turnover. At times they exceeded home sales but in more recent years they have settled down and currently comprise about one third of the total turnover. They are, of course, a major factor in the success of the company, which currently exports to about 35 countries from Canada to Kazakhstan. Whilst exporting successfully offers incredible potential for growth, it also offers stability. With Teagles' experience in France still fresh in some memories, the directors

The Teagle directors: Geoff Osborne, Roger Teagle, Duncan Wilson, David Teagle, Jon Cox, Fred Teagle, John Teagle and Tom Teagle

The 2014 stand at the November Eurotier exhibition in Hannover, featuring the new Telehawk straw bedder.

are well aware that a greater number and geographic spread of customers reduce the risks posed by currency, changing farming methods, or the ebb and flow of distributor fortunes. Teagles' presence around the world also offers a window into what is around the corner. Trends in agriculture that emerge in one region can develop in popularity and spread. If these trends and the opportunities that they offer are identified early then a competitive advantage can be gained.

We have talked of Teagles as a major employer and a glance at the figures makes fascinating reading. The workforce in 1969 was about 140 but by the 1980s, for the reasons mentioned elsewhere, it had dropped back to about 60. From then to the present time, however, it has grown steadily and is now a little above

the 1969 level. This simple comparison, however, completely masks what has happened within the company. Because of technological advances there have been considerable differences to the composition of staff over the 45 years or so. The extensive use of "state of the art" machinery has drastically cut the man-hours required to produce a typical product. Even the simple tipping cart of 1937 could now be produced in a fraction of the time taken by those early employees. The shop-floor machines are far more complex than earlier versions and many rely on operatives making a far greater technical input than their predecessors. Conversely, there has been a large and very necessary growth in technical and sales staff to provide the back-room expertise and to achieve the sales in an increasingly competitive world.

The new Shop 4A – another 1500m² of manufacturing space

Tom Teagle was a man driven by change and excited by the possibilities presented through the use of the latest technology. He would undoubtedly be delighted at the continued developments within his company.

Fred Teagle's conclusion in the 50th anniversary book is as true now as when he wrote it and it is therefore appropriate to include this paraphrased version here: "It has been the influence of our worldwide customer base that has helped to smooth out many of the fluctuations the company has felt over the years. Our policy of looking ever further for new markets and new customers has paid dividends with new markets beginning to emerge both in North America and the Far East. In looking forward we see an ever-demanding future with more machines to be designed, more markets to be conquered, more customers to be supplied and machine qualities to be maintained and improved.

I am confident that the history and tradition of the company, together with our innovative design department and our modern manufacturing base, will enable the company to hold its position in the market place for the foreseeable future."

Appendix

Abridged list of Teagle machinery development

1937	Farm Carts and Trailers
1938	Prototype Transplanter and Home Made Tractor
1939	Tractor Tipping Trailers
1941	Mk l Two Row Semi-Automatic Potato Planter with fertilizer placement
1942	Tractor Mounted Steerage Toolbar
1943	February - W. T. Teagle (Machinery) Limited, was incorporated
	Prototype tractor mounted Crop Sprayer fitted on Standard Fordson
1944	Trailed Two Row Transplanters and Potato Planters
1945	Three Point Linkage Mounted Transplanters and Potato Planters
1946	Prototype Loader Stacker mounted on MM model UTS tractor
1948	Loader Stackers fitted to Fordson Major E27N Tractors
1949	Prototype Trailed Broadcaster
1950	Mk.1 Trailed Broadcaster
1951	Five row, Three Point Linkage Mounted Combined Fertilizer Seed Drills
	Three to six row Three Point Linkage Mounted Seed Drills
1952	Prototype Manual Hedge cutter fitted with Trojan Engine (called Power Tool)
	50cc Two Stroke Petrol Engine
1953	Jetcut Chain Drive fitted with Teagle Engine
	Prototype Bi-level Elevator
	Mk.2 Trailed Broadcaster
	50cc Cycle Motor attachment
1954	Single Chain Bi-Level Elevator
1955	Belt Driven Low Bin Mounted Broadcaster with a primitive 'Arc Control' spreading mechanism
1956	High Bin Mounted Broadcaster with Arc Control spreading mechanism
	Jetso Planter Frame, with Transplanter, Potato Planter, Fertilizer Box, and Seed Drill options
	Model C Twin Chain Slatted Multi-Level Elevator.
1957	Jetscythe
	Hi and Lo Seed Drills
	All planters and seed drills now called 'Jetso'
	Jettiller with gearbox drive situated inside the wheel
	S.C.M. Single Chain Multilevel Elevator
	LL/A. LL/B, and LL/C Industrial Elevators
	2S Lo-Bin and 7S Hi-Bin Gear Driven Mounted Broadcasters
	Digo Garden Cultivator
1958	Zup Automatic pick-up Elevator with 4 Wheel Steering
	Shaft Drive Jetcut with Open Bevel Gears
	Spudnick Potato Harvester
	Tracut Tractor Mounted Hedge Trimmer
	Series B2 126cc 4 Stroke Petrol Engine
1959	Spudnick Potato Harvester with drum elevator
	Gearbox Reduction Drive on all Multilevel Elevators
	Jettiller with 4 Stroke Engine and optional Rotary Cultivator
	4 ton Grain Trailer
	Single and Two Row Mounted Potato Diggers
	Supreme Trailer Spreader
	Supreme Tipping Trailer Spreader

	Tracut with Retractable Arm
	Tipmix Cement Mixer with Roll Grip Tyre Drive
	New Model 'C' Extended Elevator (later called Major 'C')
1960	Potato Haulm Pulveriser
	Model XL Trailer Spreader
1961	Versatile Broadcaster
	Speediloader Automatic Pickup Elevator
	Series C1 4 Stroke Petrol Engine fitted with Wipac Magister Magneto
1962	Tipmix with Gear Drive
	AT1 Hay Tedder
	Senior Trailer Spreader
	Junior Trailer Spreader
	DD Two Row Potato Digger
	LPD/C Single Row Potato Digger
	Silver Bullet Tracut Hedgetrimmer with 'Fingertip Control'
	Mid Mounted Silver Bullet Tracut Hedgetrimmer with 'Fingertip Control'
	Model 5/120 Potato Harvester.
1963	Scimitar Potato Haulm Pulveriser
	Prototype Crop Ventilating Fans
	Rear Mounted Side Spreader - later named Spread-A-Box
1964	Crop Drying Fans with circular outlets
	Super Jetcut Shaft Drive - Enclosed Gears
	Super Jetcut Attachment for Stihl Chainsaw
	AT2 - 2 Row Hay Tedder
	AT3 - 3 Row Hay Tedder
	7/130 Potato Harvester
	Golden Bullet Tracut Hedgetrimmer - Gearbox Drive
1965	Jettiller with Briggs and Stratton Engine
	Jetscythe with Briggs and Stratton Engine
	Speediloader with Ground Drive
	Thermo-blast TMF/A1 and TMF/B1 Crop Drying Fans (Square Outlets)
1966	Universal Tipmix
	Rapide Elevator
	1200 Mounted Broadcaster
	Prototype 6' Cut Rotary Mower
	Secondary Beater on Senior Spreaders
	Aero Bale Booster Conveyor
	Jetcut fitted with 32cc JAP engine
1967	Matchless 5', Mower
	Dominant Mk.1, 2 Swath Haymaker
	Dominant Single Swath Haymaker
1968	Aeride Elevator
	257 and 360 Side Spreaders
	Tumbleloader Automatic Pick-up Elevator and Trailer
	Dominant 4 row Haymaker
1969	720 Side Spreader
	Terrier Trailer Spreader
	Matchless Mk.3 Mower
	Prototype Titan 7 Tandem Axle Tipping Trailer
	Triumph Potato Harvester
	Tiger Trailer Spreader
1970	360 Side Spreader
	Scimitar Potato Haulm Pulveriser
	Titan 7 Trailer Spreader
	Ranger Oscillating Bale Elevator
1971	Dominant Mk 4 Haymaker
	Plastic Hoppers fitted on Versatile and 1200 Broadcasters

1972	Titan 10 Tipping Trailer
1973	Triumph 6 Tipping Trailer
	Quick Release Arc Control Plate on Versatile and 1200 Broadcasters
1974	Titan 7 and 10 ton Dump Trailers
	Lightning Tumbleloader Automatic Pick-up Elevator and Trailer
	Dynacut 300 and 400 Flail Hedgetrimmer
1975	Tipmix 50
	Dynacut Hydra Control Series A and Mk 2 Hedgetrimmers
1977	Runabout Multilevel Elevator
	Elite Twin Hopper Broadcaster
	Mk.1 8' Pasture Topper
1978	Dynacut S and SB Hydraulic Driven Flail Hedgetrimmer
1979	Dynacut SX and SBX Flail Hedgetrimmers
	Spiromix 100 Cement Mixer
	Series 80 Broadcasters, 580, 680, 1280, 1680 and 6080 Models
1980	Hydrax Log Splitter
	Spiromix 200 Cement Mixer
	Dynacut K Flail Hedgetrimmer
	Titan 8 Mono Tipping Trailer
	Tiger 45 Tipping Trailer
	Titan 10 Mono Tipping Trailer
	Spiromix 50 Cement Mixer
	Toucan 6 and Toucan 7 Precision Chop Forage Wagons
1981	Tiger 60 Tipping Trailer
	Dynacut K Long Reach Flail Hedgetrimmer
1982	Toucan 6, 8 and 10 Precision Chop Forage Wagons
1983	Titan Super 7, 8 and 10 Trailers
	AT 22 Broadcaster
	Spiromix 200H Cement Mixer
	Trojan 550 and 700 Dual Dung/ Slurry Rotary Spreader
1984	Small Square Bale Shredder
	Topper 8 Mk.2 Gearbox & Belt Drive Pasture Topper
	Tiger 60 Mono Trailer
	AT44 Broadcaster
1985	AT18 Broadcaster
	Tornado 550 and 700 Sidespreaders
	Siler Forage Harvester
1986	Spiromix 100H and 200H Hydraulic Drive Mixers
1987	Quick Hitch A Frames
	Prototype Round Bale Straw Shredder – Vertical Tub Type
	5' Round Bale Straw Shredder (called 'Tomahawk' at 1987 Smithfield Show)
1988	Tomahawk 4' and Tomahawk 5' Round Bale Straw Shredders
1989	Toucan Range, 60, 80 and 100 fitted with Teagle Harvesters
	Tornado 555 and 707 Sidespreaders
	Tomahawk 100 Small Bale Straw Shredders
	Tomahawk 400 and 500 Round Bale Straw Shredders
1990	Tomahawk 4000 and 5000 Silage Feeders
1991	Titan 80 Mono and Titan 70 Dropside Tipping Trailers
	XT18, XT22 and XT44 Broadcasters with redesigned gearboxes
	Spiromix 200F Fork Mounted Mixer
1992	Tornado 858 Sidespreader

	Prototype Tomahawk 700 Trailed Box-Type Big Bale Shredder
	XT46 Broadcaster
1993	Titan 70 Drop Side Trailer, with Grain and Silage Sides
	Topper 6 and Topper 10 Pasture Toppers
	Tornado 858T Tandem Axle Sidespreader
	Titan 10 and 80 Mono Grain Trailer with Silage Sides
	Tomahawk 404, 505, 4040 and 5050 Round Bale Feeder-Bedders
	Dynacut KX Flail Hedgetrimmer
1994	Tomahawk 606 and 6060 Feeder-Bedders
	Tomahawk 508 and 5080 Feeder-Bedders
1995	Topper 510 Pasture Topper
	Silaflow160 Swath Conditioner with Spring Tines
	Super-ted 160 Swath Conditioner
1996	Super-ted 220 Swath Conditioner
	XT20 Broadcaster
	TD50 2 ton Capacity Mounted Broadcaster
1997	Telescopic Big Bag Lifter
	Tomahawk 404M, 505M and 508M Round Bale Straw Mills
	Tomahawk 808MF Box-Type Straw Bale Bedder
1998	Topper 4
	Tomahawk 8080 Box-Type Feeder-Bedders
	Tomahawk 8080S Swivel Chute Feeder-Bedders
1999	Topper 8 Offset
	Tomahawk 8080TC Twin Chute Feeder-Bedders
2000	Le Boulch Rear Discharge Spreaders Imported
	Tomahawk 9090 Feeder-Bedder
2001	Topper 5
	S60 Broadcaster – later called Top-line S60
	Tomahawk 8080 Single Cross Beater Feeder-Bedder
2002	Berti Flail Mowers imported
2003	Tomahawk 808S Mounted Straw Bedder
	Topper 9
2004	XT24 and XT48 Broadcasters
	Dynamo 120, 150 and 180 Finishing Mowers
	XT20 Broadcaster
	Compact 8 Broadcaster
2005	Dynamo Engine Drive Finishing Mowers
2006	Tomahawk Dual-Chop versions introduced
	SC Sloping Chutes fitted to all models of Box-Type Tomahawks
2007	EF120 Engine Driven Trailed Flail Mower
2008	T505ME Electric Powered Drum Tomahawk Mills
2009	Tomahawk 8080WB Wide Body Feeder-Bedder
	Dynamo 245 Finishing Mower
	Commence Importing Tulip Equipment
2010	Cassette Blade holders on Tomahawk Dual-Chop Machines
	Tomahawk 1010 Feeder-Bedders
2011	Titan 10 and 12 Rear Discharge Spreaders
2012	Tomahawk 1010 fitted with Weigh Cells
	Tomahawk 505XL and 505XLM Large Capacity Drum Feeder-Bedders
	Restyling and Re-launch of the complete Tomahawk Range of Flow Plus Machines
	T8100 and T8150 Standard width, and T8500 and T8550 Wide Bodied Machines
2013	Super-ted 221
	Titan 6, 8, 9, Rear Discharge Spreaders
	Tomahawk 7100 and 7150 Mounted Feeder-Bedders
2014	Telehawk Bedder for mounting on Telescopic Loaders